NutriBullet Recipe Book:

Slim Smoothies

81 Super Healthy & Fat Burning NutriBullet Smoothie Recipes to Lose Weight and Enhance Health

By: *Diana Clayton*

Disclaimer:

This book is written to supplement the Nutribullet Nutrition Extractor and has no affiliation with Nutribullet LLC. NutriBullet LLC was not involved in the recipe creation or development of this book.

Every effort has been made to ensure that the information in this book is accurate and complete, however, the author and the publisher do not warrant the accuracy of the information, text and graphics contained within the book due to the rapidly changing nature of science and research. The author and the publisher do not hold any responsibility for errors, omissions or contrary interpretation of the subject matter herein.

Table of Contents

Immune Support Smoothies....................27

Weight Loss Smoothies....................37

Protein & 'Dessert' Smoothies 53

Cleanse and Detox Smoothies 63

Introduction

Go into your kitchen now, open the cupboards and throw away every single piece of blitzing equipment you have. Throw out the big blenders, throw out the stick blenders, and throw out the things you bought while watching infomercials that promised the earth and delivered none of the things they purported to – throw them into the trash. Now get into your car, go to the store and purchase a NutriBullet, come home and give it pride of place on the kitchen counter, for this is all you will need to meet your smoothie making needs.

Ok, so that was a little melodramatic, but I think you get the point. The NutriBullet truly is *the* sports car amongst the station wagons. Its strong powerful base houses the heart of the NutriBullet – its 600-900 watt high torque motor that is so powerful it can obliterate ANYTHING in seconds! Coupled with its stainless steel extractor blades that never need sharpening, it causes a cyclonic action that breaks through everything from skins and stems to seeds and nuts. It will handle anything you throw in it. And this is what makes the NutriBullet completely unique and a cut above many other blenders. This fantastic unique design enables you to extract the maximum nutrition from your ingredients, because it pulverizes all the cells allowing all the vitamins, minerals and nutrients to explode out. The NutriBullet also has a milling blade, which is a flat blade specifically designed for blending tougher substances like grains or for grinding up herbs. If you are serious about smoothies, the NutriBullet is one piece of machinery you definitely don't want to be without.

The importance of *healthy* smoothies

All smoothies are *not* created equal. If you get your daily smoothie from your local restaurant chain, ice cream shop, or venue, then chances are you aren't eating anything much healthier than ice cream itself. In fact, many of these smoothies are more calorie dense than a double cheeseburger from McDonald's and a medium fry. (And sadly, you thought you were choosing the healthier option). Unfortunately, with all of the added sugars, sherbets, and preservatives what you end up with is a 'liquid candy' with characteristics similar to a soda beverage.

Now, don't get me wrong, I'm all for a drink that tastes addictively delicious, but if I have to raise my blood pressure to get it, then I'm not interested. And that is why *you* need to be in charge of what *you* put into your smoothies (and into your body for that matter). If you're looking for amazing smoothies that won't weigh you down and instead tremendously enhance your health and energy, then it has to start with you in your kitchen.

With new ground breaking research emerging all the time, never has the spotlight been on the importance of fruits and vegetables like it is now. They are loaded with anti-oxidants which protect the body from free radical damage which has relevance not only for general health and the ability to ward off diseases, but anti-oxidants are the new botox. They are being heralded as the natural fountain of youth we have all been searching for as new research has shown their role in helping to reverse and delay the appearance of the visible signs of aging. If the idea of a facelift without the pain hasn't sold you, then how about the high levels of vitamins, phyto-chemicals and minerals that reside in these food groups? There is a reason for the age old adage "an apple a day keeps the doctor away" – and this is becoming true of not just apples, but of all fruits, and vegetables. If we want to be healthy and ward off the ever mounting number of illnesses that seem to plague modern society, then we MUST start giving priority to fruits and vegetables as part of our daily diets.

Ideally, you want to get your kids in on it and the younger you get them on board the better. Make fruit and veg part of their diet from the time they are babies and they will develop a taste for the good things in life.

Smoothies are without a doubt the way forward on the human races quest for health and vitality. Easy and quick to make, there are no more excuses for not being a "smooth-a-holic."

BUT folks, while smoothies are an amazing source of nutrition – a complete meal in a glass – if you want to kick it up to a whole new level, you are going to want to cross the threshold into the wondrous world of GREEN SMOOTHIES!

Why Go Green?

You will notice that many of the smoothies in this book are green smoothies. That's not by accident. Green fruit and veggies just take your healthy smoothie experience from wow to EXTRAORDINARY.

Leafy greens are packed full of the most amazing nutrition that your body just cannot afford to do without. Many people get confused and think when we talk about green smoothies we mean taking a whole bunch of spinach and broccoli and liquidizing it, holding your nose and chugging it down while fighting the urge to throw it right back up – and that folks is not what green smoothies are about at all. Just as regular smoothies can be a taste extravaganza, so can the ones with green ingredients. Green does not necessarily refer to the color of the finished product (although depending on your ingredients and quantities, they can certainly be green), it simply means that your regular smoothie contains one or more green ingredients. Now don't get me wrong, I realize that sometimes the finished result won't look as pretty as a beautiful strawberry smoothie, but it can certainly taste just as wonderful. And with all of the extra benefits, you simply cannot afford to ignore the health advantages of greens anymore.

Combining your fruits with some greens means your sugar consumption is reduced and what you do consume with the added fruits provides a more stable energy release. This prevents the dips in focus and concentration while keeping your body fuelled for success. Drinking your greens is the number one way to enhance your energy and mental clarity.

Fiber Fiber Fiber – we can never get enough fiber in our diet and greens are loaded with it. Fiber keeps you regular. A digestive system that works regularly helps to flush out toxins, keeps your metabolism working properly and decreases the risk of bowel and colon cancer. Fiber keeps you full between meals and helps to keep snacking at bay. It also helps to keep the bad cholesterol levels down and helps to regulate the sugar release from the fruits. All round fiber is just great!

Greens and most especially the leafy kind help to keep your body in an alkaline state. This is especially important in our modern world where our diets consist of heavily processed foods, meat and dairy and refined sugars – all of which send your body into an acidic state. The body naturally tries to right this imbalance by leaching the calcium out of your bones, resulting in bone density depletion. This then leads to a host of osteo-related problems which can all be avoided if you just sip on a green smoothie every day.

Greens contain chlorophyll which is the pigment that gives them their green color. Chlorophyll has been shown to be a powerful cancer preventative. Chlorophyll does not survive the cooking process, so eating some steamed broccoli is just not going to do it. The only way to ensure you get these cancer fighting properties into your body is to eat your greens raw.

Which brings me onto one of the best benefits of smoothies – they ARE raw! Scientists are suggesting that the best way to maximize the nutrition we receive from our fruits and veggies especially, is to puree them raw. Blitzing them up in a blender causes every single cell to burst – that means every single ounce of nutrition is ready and available for absorption. Further to this, by drinking your greens, your body does not have to work nearly as hard to extract the goodness from the food as by liquidizing it, it is primed for absorption. Every ounce of nutrition then gets absorbed and can be utilized in the body almost immediately.

So how do you get your fruits and veggies completely liquid? I have heard so many people complaining about "bits" in their smoothies or their straws getting clogged up with parts of fruit or veggies that haven't been pulverized. Fortunately the answer is as simple as a smoothie! And if you have purchased this book then chances are, you already know that the answer is the NutriBullet.

So without further ado, read on and get busy blending up some of the following 81 NutriBullet smoothie recipes. I hope you enjoy them as much as I do...

Beginner and Kid Friendly Smoothies

Getting started with green smoothies can be a daunting prospect especially if this whole lifestyle is new to you. The best way to make this a lifestyle is to include the whole family. Yes, that's right that means your kids as well! Now don't worry, I am not setting you up for major food rebellion with tons of screaming tantrums because I have a few tricks up my sleeve. For your ease and convenience I have divided this section up into 3 parts. If you follow these in sequence, before you know it, any tantrums will be for more smoothies!

The first 3 smoothies are for those who are just starting out on their green smoothie journey and are the most child friendly. In this regard, taste is foremost on the agenda. The most important goal when introducing your children to smoothies is that they drink them! The nutritional variety and balance can be achieved at a later stage, but only if the child is open to, and enjoys drinking smoothies. When asking a child to drink smoothies through a straw it is important that that they are able to do it. The smoothie shouldn't be too thick as this will discourage the child and make it a negative experience. So, always do a quick taste test yourself to ensure that it is of course flavorful, but that you can also drink it easily through the straw.

Children these days are accustomed to drinking sweet drinks. Anything with a 'different' or unusual taste won't be easily accepted. The ingredients for the beginner smoothies have been chosen for their high natural sugar content and sweetness. This sweetness masks the flavor of the green ingredients that most probably are not used to consuming in their raw state. At this stage you can add natural sweeteners if the child needs it. Remember, we want to keep our smoothies as healthy as possible, so always go for all natural sweeteners like maple syrup, honey, stevia, and dates if needed. Also, keep in mind that some kids refuse to drink green smoothies based on the color alone. So if you're concerned about that, try serving the smoothie in an opaque cup with a top and a straw. Works every time!

Smoothies 4-6 are for intermediate green smoothie drinkers. These should only be introduced once your child is happily drinking the beginner smoothies with enjoyment. The intermediate experience smoothie has a little less sweetness as it doesn't depend on cacao or peanut butter to mask the greens, but just the sweetness of the fruits and fruit juices themselves. They have more ingredients to help round out and improve the nutritional content and your child will start feeling the health benefits.

Smoothies 7-9 are for experienced kids. Now you can really start playing with the combinations and ingredients as they have grown accustomed to the texture and their palate can handle the flavor of raw greens better. They are less reliant on the sweetness to drink it and so you can begin upping the greens to include more unusual vegetables.

So here is your guide on how to create smoothie loving kids in 3 easy steps – go forth and conquer!

Chocolate Banana Smoothie

If you're new to green smoothies or having a hard time actually enjoying them, then this is a great place to start. Almost everyone enjoys milkshakes, so this golden banana, apple, peanut butter and cacao flavored 'milkshake' below is a guaranteed winner! It is a very nutritious smoothie too! Once you're comfortable, you may want start adding a little bit more spinach each time. Another variation of this smoothie is to omit the apple and use 2 bananas instead, 120ml more of almond milk, and a little vanilla extract. It's rather delicious either way.

Yields: 2 Servings

Ingredients:

- 1 handful of spinach
- 1 frozen banana
- 1 apple, cored
- 2 tablespoons natural peanut butter
- 3 tablespoons raw cacao powder
- 2 tablespoons raw honey
- cinnamon to taste
- 360ml unsweetened almond milk

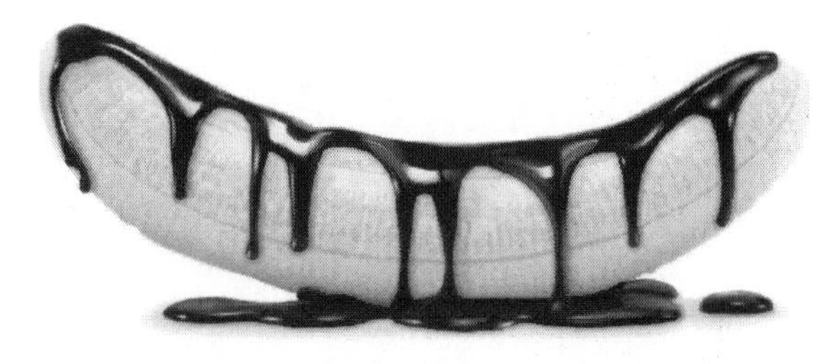

Directions:

1. Place all of the dry ingredients into your large NutriBullet cup and fire it up until smooth.
2. Garnish with a twisty or bendy straw.
3. Slurp down!

Health Benefits:

- ✓ Very high in vitamins A,B6, and E
- ✓ High in calcium
- ✓ Cholesterol free!

Nutritional values per serving: Calories: 327; Total Fat: 11.8g; Cholesterol: 0mg; Sodium: 226mg; Potassium 635mg; Carbohydrates: 50.9g; Protein: 5.8g

Cacao Raspberry Smoothie

Who knew a healthy green smoothie could taste *soooo* good? This delicious chocolate raspberry smoothie is sure to become a family favorite. And the best part? It's a lovely deep chocolate brown color, so the appearance and the taste leave not even a hint of green spinach. Even my 4 year old loves it! Remember, do not skimp on the sweetener. You don't have to use stevia but you must use a healthy sweetener of some kind as cacao is very bitter without it.

Yields: 1 Serving

Ingredients:

- 1 handful of spinach
- 130g frozen raspberries
- 2 tablespoons raw cacao powder
- 240ml unsweetened almond milk
- ½ tsp vanilla extract (optional)
- Stevia to taste

Directions:

1. Toss all the ingredients into your NutriBullet and power it up until smooth.
2. Pour and garnish with a twisty/bendy straw and a few raspberries.
3. Enjoy!

Health Benefits:

- ✓ Very high in vitamins A, C, and E
- ✓ Very high in calcium
- ✓ Very high in manganese
- ✓ Very high in dietary fiber
- ✓ Cholesterol free!

Nutritional values per serving: Calories: 165; Total Fat: 5.8g; Cholesterol: 0mg; Sodium: 210mg; Potassium: 526mg; Carbohydrates: 21.2g; Protein: 3.3g

Shhhh... It's Spinach Smoothie

Here is yet another amazingly delicious smoothie that hides the taste of spinach very well. It is a classic smoothie recipe and more than likely you'll always have all of the ingredients on hand. So it is usually in heavy rotation in my home. The banana, berries, and peanut butter create an amazing flavor and all of the ingredients are packed with the vitamins, nutrients, fiber, and protein that your body needs.

Yields: 2 Servings

Ingredients:

- 1 handful of spinach
- 1 frozen banana
- 150g of mixed berries
- 1 tablespoon natural peanut butter
- 240ml unsweetened almond milk

Directions:

1. Combine all the ingredients in your NutriBullet and blitz until smooth.
2. Drink and grow smart from all the vitamins!

Health Benefits:

- ✓ Very high in vitamins A, B6, C, and E
- ✓ High in dietary fiber
- ✓ High in manganese
- ✓ High in calcium
- ✓ Cholesterol free!

Nutritional values per serving: Calories: 160; Total Fat: 5.6g; Cholesterol: 0mg; Sodium: 140mg; Potassium: 488mg; Carbohydrates: 26.6g; Protein: 4.1g

Island Style Smoothie

I know what you're thinking... parsley in a smoothie? But trust me, this smoothie almost tastes like dessert. The combination of apple, pineapple, banana, and mango leaves just a hint of the parsley in this smoothie which provides a subtle, yet unique and refreshing taste. Plus, parsley kills bacteria in the body and is used to treat many illnesses. And all this time you thought it was just for decoration. Bottoms up!

Yields: 2 Servings

Ingredients:

- ½ apple – cored
- ½ frozen banana
- 180g fresh or frozen pineapple
- 165g chopped mango
- 15g fresh parsley chopped and stems cut
- Coconut water to max line

Directions:

1. Pour all the ingredients into your NutriBullet and blast them until smooth.
2. Decant the smoothie into two suitable cups and garnish with a cocktail umbrella.
3. Drink up and think of your idyllic island vista!

Note: *It is <u>not</u> recommended to consume parsley if you are expecting.*

Health Benefits:

- ✓ Very high in vitamins A, B6, and C
- ✓ Very high in manganese
- ✓ High in dietary fiber
- ✓ High in potassium and magnesium
- ✓ Low in saturated fat
- ✓ Cholesterol free!

Nutritional values per serving: Calories: 210; Total Fat: 0.9g; Cholesterol: 0mg; Sodium: 260mg; Potassium: 1060mg; Carbohydrates: 52.6g; Protein: 3.3g

Blueberry Pomegranate Smoothie

A wonderful smoothie for green smoothie newbies. The blend of the apple and blueberries with the pomegranate juice completely masks the fact that there is spinach in this smoothie. The NutriBullet obliterates the frozen banana as well as the leaves of the spinach. This eliminates the 'bits' that might put some off smoothies. The ingredients are also all rich in vitamins and low in calories, making it ideal for those concerned about their weight.

Yields: 2 Servings

Ingredients:

- 1 handful of spinach
- ½ apple
- 1 frozen banana
- 75g blueberries
- 240ml 100% pomegranate juice (or substitute orange juice)

Directions:

1. Place all the ingredients into the NutriBullet and blaze away until smooth.
2. Suck down your yummy medley of fruits!

Health Benefits:

- ✓ High in vitamins A, B6, and C
- ✓ High in potassium
- ✓ Very low in sodium
- ✓ Very low in saturated fat
- ✓ Cholesterol free!

Nutritional values per serving: Calories: 170; Total Fat: 0.2g; Cholesterol: 0mg; Sodium: 18mg; Potassium: 672mg; Carbohydrates: 44g; Protein: 1.3g

Very Berry Smoothie

This berry bonanza is bursting with flavors and nutrients. The orange juice adds a natural sweetness that will cover any slightly salty flavor from the spinach, while the remaining ingredients create a deliciously smooth and nutritious smoothie to enjoy every day.

Yields: 2 Servings

Ingredients:

- 1 handful of spinach
- 1 frozen banana
- 225g mixed berries
- 240ml fresh orange juice

Directions:

1. Tip all the ingredients into the NutriBullet and fire away until smooth.
2. Guzzle down and grow healthy!

Health Benefits:

- ✓ Very high in vitamins A, B6, and C
- ✓ High in manganese
- ✓ High in dietary fiber
- ✓ High in potassium
- ✓ Very low in sodium
- ✓ Very low in saturated fat
- ✓ Cholesterol free!

Nutritional values per serving: Calories: 151; Total Fat: 0.7g; Cholesterol: 0mg; Sodium: 14mg; Potassium: 700mg; Carbohydrates: 36.1g; Protein: 2.7g

Green Irish Kiwi Smoothie

The ingredients in this smoothie will all add to its 'Irish' green hue. The complex flavor created by combining the kiwi fruit, grapes, banana, and apple juice will definitely cover any hint of spinach. I've enjoyed this smoothie with many variations. Once you're more comfortable with green smoothies, you can use coconut water or unsweetened almond milk instead of apple juice or even add a cup of nonfat Greek yoghurt. Either way, you can't lose.

Yields: 2 Servings

Ingredients:

- 1 handful of spinach
- ½ frozen banana
- 2 kiwi fruit, peeled and halved
- 92g green seedless grapes (optional)
- 120ml apple juice

Directions:

1. Place all the ingredients in your NutriBullet and fire it up until smooth.
2. Pour and garnish with a 'four leaf clover' and a twisty/bendy straw.
3. Sip this yummy smoothie and think of leprechauns!

Health Benefits:

- ✓ Very high in vitamins A and C
- ✓ High in dietary fiber
- ✓ High in potassium
- ✓ Very low in sodium
- ✓ Very low in saturated fat
- ✓ Cholesterol free!

Nutritional values per serving: Calories: 136; Total Fat: 0.7g; Cholesterol: 0mg; Sodium: 17mg; Potassium: 588mg; Carbohydrates: 33.5g; Protein: 1.9g

Honeybee Smoothie

The Romaine lettuce, while rich in vitamins and minerals does not have a strong flavor when compared to the other ingredients in this smoothie. So this makes for a perfect green smoothie for beginners. The honeydew melon and the mango will be the dominant flavors with a delicious hint of blackberry.

Yields: 2 Servings

Ingredients:

- 1-2 handfuls chopped romaine lettuce
- 170g Honeydew melon
- 250g mango, chopped
- 75g blackberries (or other berries)
- 1 tablespoon honey or to taste
- Ice as needed
- 120ml water

Directions:

1. Place all the ingredients into the NutriBullet and fire it up until smooth.
2. Sip and think of peaceful meadows.

Health Benefits:

- ✓ Very high in vitamins A, B6, and C
- ✓ High in dietary fiber
- ✓ High in magnesium
- ✓ Low in sodium
- ✓ Very low in saturated fat
- ✓ Cholesterol free!

Nutritional values per serving: Calories: 163; Total Fat: 3.4g; Cholesterol: 0mg; Sodium: 42mg; Potassium: 439mg; Carbohydrates: 23.7g; Protein: 4.7g

Aztec Mango Smoothie

The Aztec warriors used to use chia seeds as their 'trail mix'. They could march for great distances with only a couple of handfuls of chia seeds to sustain them. The oranges, strawberries, banana, and mango are great tasting and combined with the lemon juice will cover any unpalatable flavors. The NutriBullet will smash the chia seeds so that there are no 'bits'.

Yields: 2 Servings

Ingredients:

- 1 handful of spinach
- 165g mango, chopped
- ½ frozen banana
- 2 oranges, peeled
- 4 strawberries
- Juice of ½ lemon
- 2 tablespoons chia seeds
- 240ml water

Directions:

1. Combine all the ingredients in your NutriBullet and blitz until smooth.
2. Drink and enjoy!

Health Benefits:

- ✓ Very high in vitamins A and C
- ✓ Very high in dietary fiber
- ✓ Very low in sodium
- ✓ Very low in saturated fat
- ✓ Cholesterol free!

Nutritional values per serving: Calories: 238; Total Fat: 3.6g; Cholesterol: 0mg; Sodium: 14mg; Potassium 751mg; Carbohydrates: 49g; Protein: 6g

Heart Healthy Smoothies

The heart is the most important organ in the body. Most people consider the brain to be the most important organ in the body as it is the seat of all our higher order functions, but technically you are still classed as alive when your brain is dead and this is solely because your heart remains beating. Once the heart beats for the last time everything else dies too. The heart has the biggest role of responsibility in the body as everything else depends on it. It is therefore vital that we take every precaution to protect the heart and keep it functioning optimally.

Heart health is becoming an increasing cause for concern with the sudden rise in incidence of heart disease and chronic heart conditions. At the root of this wide spread degeneration in overall heart health is what we put into our bodies. Our food is too fatty, too rich, and packed full of all the wrong things – it's that simple! If we want to take care of our heart we need to clean up our diets. Now while we might all know that eating certain foods are better for us, it is often difficult to change eating habits that have become entrenched over many years. With this in mind there are a number of small steps you can take to put you on the road to a healthy heart and fortunately most of these are able to be incorporated into your new smoothie lifestyle.

Fruits and vegetables are your one way ticket to a healthy heart because they are loaded with vitamins and minerals that specifically fight off cardiovascular disease. There is no easier way to get enough fruit and vegetables into your daily diet than through smoothies. Limit the inclusion of unhealthy fats and cholesterol in your diet. They add no value to your body and only succeed in clogging up your arteries and paving the way for a heart attack. Make sure you limit the amount of sodium you consume. Sodium leads to high blood pressure which puts strain on your heart by making it pump faster than it is supposed to. Limiting processed foods will go a long way to reduce sodium intake as these are typically loaded with hidden salts that you are probably not even aware you are consuming. Flavor your food and your smoothies with a selection of fresh herbs and spices instead. These small changes to your daily diet will see you reaping the benefits of good heart health for years to come.

Prevention is far better (and easier) than cure! Rather take the necessary steps to keep your heart healthy than try to reverse damage already done to your heart.

A very good way to prevent the development of heart problems is to include one or more of the following heart healthy ingredients into your smoothies. Oats and flax seeds are excellent whole grains that offer protection to the heart. Soy products are excellent for a healthy heart. Other superb additions to your smoothies include foods like broccoli, spinach, okra, apples, green tea, flax seeds, almonds, walnuts, oats, raw cacao powder, pomegranate juice, carrots, blueberries, cherries, papaya/pawpaw, oranges, and bananas to get a boost of heart healthy nutrition injected straight into your heart!

Heart Disease Dusting Smoothie

Delicious and nutritious! Adding just a few baby carrots to your daily diet can drastically help to fight heart disease, while spinach has just about everything your heart needs. An apple a day cuts heart disease risk by up 40% and oranges contain hesperidin which improves blood vessel function thus lowering the risk of contracting heart disease all together. This smoothie has everything your little heart desires (and needs).

Yields: 2 Servings

Ingredients:

- 1-2 handfuls of spinach
- 1 apple
- 1 medium carrot
- 1 orange
- Pinch of ground ginger
- Pinch of cinnamon
- Juice of ½ lemon
- Water to max line

Directions:

1. Throw all the ingredients into your large NutriBullet cup and blitz until smooth.
2. Consume and live longer!

Health Benefits:

- ✓ Very high in vitamins A, B6 and C
- ✓ Very low in saturated fat
- ✓ Low in sodium
- ✓ Cholesterol free!

Nutritional values per serving: Calories: 115; Total Fat: .3g; Cholesterol: 0mg; Sodium: 46mg; Potassium: 551mg; Carbohydrates: 29.1g; Protein: 2.1g

Green Tea Banana Smoothie

Bananas are *loaded* with potassium which is one of the most important nutrients for keeping the heart healthy. The potassium in the banana keeps the fluid and salt levels in the body in a perfect state of balance while helping to lower blood pressure and regulate heart rhythm. Drinking delicious Green tea on a daily basis reduces your risk of heart attack and stroke and even helps to prevent certain cancers. Did I fail to mention how tasty this smoothie is? Try it, have a heart.

Yields: 2 Servings

Ingredients:

- 1-2 handfuls of spinach
- 1 frozen banana
- 140g seedless green grapes
- 240ml green tea
- 2 tsp honey
- 1 tablespoon ground flax seeds

Directions:

1. Pour steaming hot water into a glass and add 2 green tea bags. Allow to brew for 3 minutes. Remove tea bags, add honey, and stir. Let tea cool to room temperature.
2. Combine all the ingredients in your large NutriBullet cup and blitz until smooth.
3. Drink and be happy!

Health Benefits:

- ✓ Very high in vitamin A and B6
- ✓ High in manganese
- ✓ High in dietary fiber
- ✓ Low in sodium
- ✓ Low in saturated fat
- ✓ Cholesterol free!

Nutritional values per serving: Calories: 145; Total Fat: 1.5 g; Cholesterol: 0mg; Sodium: 27mg; Potassium: 551mg; Carbohydrates: 33.1g; Protein: 2.5g

Cacao Dream Smoothie

Raw cacao is not only soooo good, but it is an antioxidant powerhouse! Containing more antioxidants by weight than blueberries, pomegranates, acai, and goji berries combined, it is the ultimate guilt free treat. *Plus* it's great for the heart since it has a blood-thinning effect. The flax seeds in this smoothie add an additional boost of heart protection. So enjoy this delicious cacao smoothie guilt free!

Yields: 2 Servings

Ingredients:

- 1-2 handfuls of kale
- 2 kiwi fruit
- 1 frozen banana
- 180g fresh or frozen pineapple
- 1 tablespoon cacao powder
- Several mint leaves
- Stevia to taste
- 1 tablespoon ground flax seeds
- 120ml-240ml water

Directions:

1. Tip all the ingredients into your large NutriBullet cup and fire away until smooth.
2. Guzzle down and grow healthy!

Health Benefits:

- ✓ Very high in vitamin A, B6, and C
- ✓ High in potassium, magnesium and manganese
- ✓ High in dietary fiber
- ✓ Very low in sodium
- ✓ Cholesterol free!

Nutritional values per serving: Calories: 153; Total Fat: 1.9g; Cholesterol: 0mg; Sodium: 37mg; Potassium: 759mg; Carbohydrates: 33.1g; Protein: 4.8g

Tropical Almond Smoothie

Almonds are rich in good fats which help lower the levels of bad cholesterol 'LDL' and raise the levels of good cholesterol 'HDL'. Blueberries are rich in heart healthy phytochemicals and antioxidants and they also contain significant amounts of fiber. Papaya/pawpaw and broccoli simply cannot be ignored when it comes to the heart health, as they both do *wonders* for the heart.

Yields: 2 Servings

Ingredients:

- 50g frozen broccoli
- 75g papaya/pawpaw
- 1 frozen banana
- 180g pineapple, fresh or frozen
- 75g blueberries
- 27g slivered almonds
- Water to max line

Directions:

1. Tip all the ingredients into your large NutriBullet cup and fire away until smooth.
2. Sip and grow strong!

Health Benefits:

- ✓ Very high in vitamins B6 and C
- ✓ High in manganese
- ✓ Very low in sodium
- ✓ Low in saturated fat
- ✓ Cholesterol free!

Nutritional values per serving: Calories: 210; Total Fat: 6.4g; Cholesterol: 0mg; Sodium: 12mg; Potassium: 554mg; Carbohydrates: 37.5g; Protein: 4.6g

The A-celer-ator Smoothie

Celery is great because it is loaded with phytochemicals called phthalide which help the muscles in your arterial walls relax and smooth out. This lowers blood pressure making it easier for your heart to pump. This is a lovely smoothie to enjoy in the morning and it's quite refreshing.

Yields: 2 Servings

Ingredients:

- 1 medium stalk of celery
- 170g honeydew melon
- ½ large cucumber
- 1 pear
- Juice of ½ lime
- Few mint leaves
- 60ml water
- Ice as needed

Directions:

1. Combine all the ingredients in your large NutriBullet cup and blitz until smooth.
2. Sip this yummy smoothie and relax!

Health Benefits:

- ✓ Very high in vitamins B6 and C
- ✓ High in potassium
- ✓ Low in sodium
- ✓ Very low in saturated fat
- ✓ High in dietary fiber
- ✓ Cholesterol free!

Nutritional values per serving: Calories: 85; Total Fat: 0.3g; Cholesterol: 0mg; Sodium: 25mg; Potassium: 422mg; Carbohydrates: 21.7g; Protein: 1.4g

The Rabbit Smoothie

This nutritious low calorie smoothie promotes health and weight loss leading to a healthy heart. Carrots are rich in antioxidants and fiber and help to fight heart disease. Antioxidants bind themselves to free radicals and limit the damage they cause to our bodies. The Romaine lettuce and the blackberries are also rich sources of antioxidants and fiber while also being packed with vitamins and minerals.

Yields: 2 Servings

Ingredients:

- 2-4 handfuls Romaine lettuce
- 165g mango
- 75g blackberries
- 1 medium carrot
- apple juice to max line

Directions:

1. Pour all the ingredients into your large NutriBullet cup and blast them until smooth.
2. Drink up and get healthy like Bugs Bunny!

Health Benefits:

- ✓ Very high in vitamins A, B6, and C
- ✓ Low in sodium
- ✓ High in manganese
- ✓ High in dietary fiber
- ✓ Very low in saturated
- ✓ Cholesterol free!

Nutritional values per serving: Calories: 146; Total Fat: 0.6g; Cholesterol: 0mg; Sodium: 30mg; Potassium: 498mg; Carbohydrates: 35.3g; Protein: 1.4g

Healthy Hemp Smoothie

Parsley is a relative of celery and is also rich in essential phytochemicals and antioxidants which help maintain circulatory health. Hemp seeds are also vitally important to heart health. They revitalize cardiovascular function and circulation as they have close to the perfect balance of omega – 3 to omega – 6 essential fatty acids. Studies show that Papaya helps to protect again heart disease, heart attacks, and stroke. This is one delicious healthy heart smoothie!

Yields: 2 Servings

Ingredients:

- 30g parsley
- 1 handful of spinach
- 8 frozen strawberries
- 290g papaya/pawpaw, chopped
- 1 tablespoon hemp seeds
- Water to max line

Directions:

1. Toss all the ingredients into your large NutriBullet cup and power it up until smooth.
2. Garnish with some heart healthy fruit slices.
3. Enjoy!

Health Benefits:

- ✓ Very high in vitamins A and C
- ✓ Very high in manganese
- ✓ High in magnesium and potassium
- ✓ High in iron
- ✓ Low in sodium
- ✓ Low in saturated fat
- ✓ High in dietary fiber
- ✓ Cholesterol free!

Nutritional values per serving: Calories: 115; Total Fat: 2.5g; Cholesterol: 0mg; Sodium: 33mg; Potassium: 576mg; Carbohydrates: 23g; Protein: 3.3g

Yogi Bear Smoothie

Fermented products and probiotics like yoghurt are great for the heart as they are said to help lower blood pressure and protect against heart disease. Studies indicate that they can improve cholesterol, and reduce blood glucose and insulin resistance. The potassium also helps control the fluid salt balance in your cells by balancing out the sodium in your body. If you're vegan, there are several delicious vegan yoghurt varieties.

Yields: 2 Servings

Ingredients:

- 205ml fat free Greek yoghurt
- 1 apple, cored and chopped
- 150g frozen blueberries
- 120ml unsweetened almond milk
- 27g walnuts or almonds

Directions:

1. Combine all the ingredients in your NutriBullet and blitz until smooth.
2. Drink and get healthy from all the vitamins!

Health Benefits:

- ✓ Very high in vitamins B6, C, and E
- ✓ High in dietary fiber
- ✓ Low in sodium
- ✓ Low in saturated fat
- ✓ Cholesterol free!

Nutritional values per serving: Calories: 220; Total Fat: 7g; Cholesterol: 0mg; Sodium: 118mg; Potassium: 283mg; Carbohydrates: 31.4g; Protein: 13g

Nutty Professor Smoothie

The cherries and the almonds are the dominant flavors in this smoothie. The apples adds some bulk and a significant amount of fiber to the smoothie. Fiber helps to contain free radical damage by keeping them in the digestive tract longer and thus allowing your body to eliminate them before they cause damage. But we all know that apples are good for the heart. Cherries on the other hand are often overlooked. A little known fact is cherries prevent inflammation linked to heart disease and gout.

Yields: 2 Servings

Ingredients:

- 2 apples – cored
- ½ frozen banana
- 155g cherries, pits removed
- 27g slivered almonds
- 1 tsp vanilla extract
- unsweetened almond milk to max line

Directions:

3. Combine all the ingredients in your NutriBullet and blitz until smooth.
4. Drink and grow smart from all the vitamins!

Health Benefits:

- ✓ Very high in vitamins B6, C, and E
- ✓ High in dietary fiber
- ✓ Very high in calcium
- ✓ Low in saturated fats
- ✓ Cholesterol free!

Nutritional values per serving: Calories: 240; Total Fat: 8.4g; Cholesterol: 0mg; Sodium: 185mg; Potassium: 576mg; Carbohydrates: 40.4g; Protein: 3.9g

Spinach Plum Smoothie

Spinach contains a wide variety of healthy vitamins and minerals. One of the lesser known but most important of these is Co-Q10 or coenzyme Q10. Co-Q10 is used to treat heart disease and is also known to prevent heart disease. Also as previously mentioned, studies have shown that green tea, when consumed regularly, reduces the risk for heart attacks. That makes this smoothie an important one for heart health.

Yields: 2 Servings

Ingredients:

- 1-2 handfuls of spinach
- 1 frozen banana
- 2 plums, seeds removed
- 165g pineapple, chopped
- 240ml green tea
- 27g walnuts

Directions:

1. Pour steaming hot water into a glass and add 2 green tea bags. Allow to brew for 3 minutes. Remove tea bags, add honey, and stir. Let tea cool to room temperature.
2. Place all the ingredients into the NutriBullet and fire it up until smooth.
3. Slurp down this delicious heart healthy smoothie.

Health Benefits:

- ✓ Very high in vitamin A, B6, and C
- ✓ Very high in manganese
- ✓ Very low in sodium
- ✓ Low in saturated fat
- ✓ Cholesterol free!

Nutritional values per serving: Calories: 217; Total Fat: 9.8g; Cholesterol: 0mg; Sodium: 26mg; Potassium: 627mg; Carbohydrates: 31.9g; Protein: 5.9g

Immune Support Smoothies

Where most people fall short is when they treat immune boosting as a seasonal activity. Right before winter everyone loads up on Vitamin C and takes all kinds of supplements to boost their immunity and ward off the germs that cause illness. What most people don't realize is that if immune support became part of your regular routine, there would be no need to try boost your immunity seasonally. Building up and keeping your immune system in peak condition is what will keep the germs at bay rather than the ebb and flow of bombarding your body with vitamins when it's cold and then slacking off as the weather warms.

Ideally, your immune system should work like a well-oiled machine, enhancing your body and fighting off germs – naturally. A diesel car is not going to run properly on regular fuel and similarly if you do not give your body the right raw materials, it too is going to chug along before breaking down. Keeping your body healthy should not be a chore and that is where smoothies come in. There is no quicker or simpler way to load your body full of all the goodness, vitamins and minerals it needs to stay healthy all year long. The longer your immune system stays strong and healthy, the more resilient and capable it will be.

So what are the right foods to include in your smoothies to keep your cellular army fighting fit? A good place to start is with foods that are high in Vitamin C, like apples, berries, citrus fruits, pawpaw, kiwi fruit, cantaloupe, grapefruit, and leafy greens. These kinds of common ingredients should form the basis of your immune boosting smoothies because they provide your body with a healthy whack of disease fighting vitamins and minerals.

BUT...Every army needs a specially trained task force and for our body, this comes in the form of superfoods. While the smoothies in the recipes below will do their part to boost your immune system, if you are able to get your hands on some of these amazing 'extras', include them in any one of these smoothies for an additional kick of potent immune boosting power. The best immune boosting superfoods for smoothies are: ginger, garlic, turmeric, ashwaganda (herb), astragalus (Chinese herb), hemp seeds, Echinacea, coconut oil, kefir, oats, barley, green tea, kombucha (Asian tea known as the "immortal health elixir"), apple cider vinegar, camu camu berry, acai berries (or the frozen acai pulp), goji berries, spirulina, honey and bee pollen. Most of these ingredients can be found at your local health store and are easily incorporated into your basic smoothie recipes.

So without further ado, here are some immune boosting smoothies that will not only knock your socks off, but knock those disease causing bugs for a six! Enjoy!

In most team sports that you watch, the front line is where the strongest players hold position.

The O.C. Smoothie

Orange juice is probably the most classically known source of vitamin C. Strawberries also rich in antioxidants and a variety of minerals, while blueberries are a treasure trove of immune supporting vitamins. This is a true explosion of immune support in a glass!

Yields: 2 Servings

Ingredients:

- 1-2 handfuls of spinach
- 1 frozen banana
- 360ml fresh orange juice
- 8 strawberries
- 75g blueberries

Directions:

1. Add the ingredients into the NutriBullet and blitz away until smooth.
2. Drink and revitalize!

Health Benefits:

- ✓ Very high in vitamins A, B6, and C
- ✓ High in potassium
- ✓ High in dietary fiber
- ✓ Low in sodium
- ✓ Very low in saturated fat
- ✓ Cholesterol free!

Nutritional values per serving: Calories: 187; Total Fat: 0.8g; Cholesterol: 0mg; Sodium: 27mg; Potassium: 889mg; Carbohydrates: 44.7g; Protein: 3.5g

Broccoli Bomb Smoothie

The broccoli in this smoothie is a great source of phytochemicals and antioxidants that help to boost immunity. All the ingredients are great sources of vitamins essential to a healthy immune system. It may take a bit getting use to the idea of broccoli in your smoothie, but give it a try. With all of the benefits, it's worth the effort.

Yields: 2 Servings

Ingredients:

- 50g frozen broccoli
- 1 frozen banana
- 65g raspberries
- 140g green grapes
- 240ml coconut water

Directions:

1. Combine all the ingredients in your NutriBullet and blitz until smooth.
2. Drink and get healthy from all the vitamins!

Health Benefits:

- ✓ Very high in vitamins B6 and C
- ✓ Very high in manganese
- ✓ High in dietary fiber
- ✓ High in potassium and magnesium
- ✓ Low in saturated fat
- ✓ Cholesterol free!

Nutritional values per serving: Calories: 145; Total Fat: 0.8g; Cholesterol: 0mg; Sodium: 136mg; Potassium: 761mg; Carbohydrates: 34.9g; Protein: 2.9g

The Two Kings Smoothie

The kale and the acai berries in this smoothie are greatly respected 'super-foods'. They both explode with vitamins, minerals, antioxidants, and phytochemicals that are extremely beneficial for boosting immunity. The kiwi fruit and mango are also good sources of immune supporting nutrients.

Yields: 2 Servings

Ingredients:

- 1-2 handfuls of kale
- 165g mango, chopped
- 2 kiwi fruit
- 1 pouch frozen acai puree
- Water to max line

Directions:

1. Toss all the ingredients into your NutriBullet and power it up until smooth.
2. Sip and enjoy!

Health Benefits:

- ✓ Very high in vitamins A, B6, and C
- ✓ Low in sodium
- ✓ High in manganese and potassium
- ✓ High in dietary fiber
- ✓ Very low in saturated fat
- ✓ Cholesterol free!

Nutritional values per serving: Calories: 172; Total Fat: 1.4g; Cholesterol: 0mg; Sodium: 35mg; Potassium: 683mg; Carbohydrates: 31.4g; Protein: 3.2g

Kiwi Kefir Smoothie

Kefir is a live culture 'yoghurt' made from different types of milk like cow's milk, soy milk, and even coconut milk. It is packed full of powerful healing qualities and contains probiotics and pre-biotics that will strengthen your digestive tract and your immune system. The kiwi, pear, and peach are rich in vitamins and dietary fiber to further aid your immune health and add a wonderful flavor.

Yields: 2 Servings

Ingredients:

- 2 kiwi fruit, peeled and halved
- 1 pear, chopped
- ½ peach, pit removed
- 240ml kefir of your choice
- 1 tsp honey
- Stevia to taste

Directions:

1. Pour all the ingredients into your NutriBullet and blast them until smooth.
2. Garnish with a slice of peach.
3. Drink up and get healthy!

Health Benefits:

- ✓ Very high in vitamins B6 and C
- ✓ High in dietary fiber
- ✓ High in calcium
- ✓ Low in sodium
- ✓ Low in cholesterol

Nutritional values per serving: Calories: 167; Total Fat: 1.8g; Cholesterol: 8mg; Sodium: 71mg; Potassium: 368mg; Carbohydrates: 34.6g; Protein: 6.3g

Coconut-Pineapple Smoothie

Coconut milk is rich in healthy fats, and is good for the heart and boosts the immune system. As an added plus it has been shown to help with weight loss. The pineapple contains bromelain, a natural anti-inflammatory, while the grapes and raisins are all packed full of antioxidants which will help build up a strong immune system.

Yields: 2 Servings

Ingredients:

- 180g fresh or frozen pineapple
- 1 apple, cored
- 92g green grapes
- 2 tablespoons raisins
- 120ml coconut milk
- 120ml of water or as needed

Directions:

1. Place all the ingredients in your NutriBullet and fire it up until smooth.
2. Drink up and salute your health!

Health Benefits:

- ✓ Very high in vitamin B6 and C
- ✓ Very high in manganese
- ✓ Very low in sodium
- ✓ Cholesterol free!

Nutritional values per serving: Calories: 284; Total Fat: 14.6g; Cholesterol: 0mg; Sodium: 13mg; Potassium: 501mg; Carbohydrates: 41.8g; Protein: 2.4g

The Perfect Pear Smoothie

Pears work wonderfully to boost the immune system because they contain antioxidants like Vitamin C and other nutrients which fight disease and free radicals. Avocadoes are rich in 'good' fatty acids and have known anti-inflammatory properties which help the body heal. Greek yoghurt is also an immune booster. This smoothie is a literal firework of immune support just waiting to explode in your body!

Yields: 2 Servings

Ingredients:

- 1-2 handfuls of kale
- 1 pear, chopped
- 92g grapes
- ½ avocado, pitted and peeled
- 270ml fat free Greek yoghurt
- 2 tablespoons fresh lime juice
- 60ml water if necessary
- Ice as needed

Directions:

1. Place all the ingredients into the NutriBullet and fire it up until smooth.
2. Garnish with an umbrella.
3. Sip and grow strong!

Health Benefits:

- ✓ Very high in vitamins A, B6, and C
- ✓ High in manganese
- ✓ Low in sodium
- ✓ Cholesterol free!

Nutritional values per serving: Calories: 283; Total Fat: 10.3g; Cholesterol: 0mg; Sodium: 128mg; Potassium: 743mg; Carbohydrates: 37.3g; Protein: 13.8g

Orange-Berry Oatmeal Smoothie

Oranges and blueberries have a high vitamin C content as well as being a great source of dietary fiber. Oats are rich in fiber and protein which helps the body recover and stay strong. And of course, Greek yoghurt is amazing for the immune system.

Yields: 2 Servings

Ingredients:

- 235g frozen blueberries
- 135ml fat free Greek yoghurt
- 1 tsp vanilla extract (optional)
- 40g rolled oats
- 240ml fresh orange juice

Directions:

1. Tip all the ingredients into the NutriBullet and fire away until smooth.
2. Glug it down and grow healthy!

Health Benefits:

- ✓ Very high in vitamins B6 and C
- ✓ Very high in manganese
- ✓ Low in saturated fat
- ✓ Low in sodium
- ✓ Cholesterol free!

Nutritional values per serving: Calories: 200; Total Fat: 1.4g; Cholesterol: 0mg; Sodium: 50mg; Potassium: 372mg; Carbohydrates: 39.5g; Protein8.2g

Peachy Keen Smoothie

Peaches are full of antioxidants that prevent auto-immune disease. They are also a great source of vitamin A. Parsley contains a ton of phytochemicals which helps to boost the immune system and also play a role in fighting many different forms of cancer, while ginger inhibits the growth of bacteria.

Yields: 2 Servings

Ingredients:

- 1-2 handfuls of spinach
- 2 peaches, pit removed
- 25g parsley – chopped
- 120ml fresh orange juice
- about ¼ inch ginger root
- ice as needed
- 1 tbsp. honey

Directions:

1. Combine all the ingredients in your NutriBullet and blitz until smooth.
2. Sip and be well!

Health Benefits:

- ✓ Very high in vitamins A, B6, and C
- ✓ High in manganese and potassium
- ✓ High in iron
- ✓ Low in sodium
- ✓ Very low in saturated fat
- ✓ Cholesterol free!

Nutritional values per serving: Calories: 113; Total Fat: 0.6g; Cholesterol: 0mg; Sodium: 33mg; Potassium566mg; Carbohydrates: 26.5g; Protein: 2.6g

Omega Boost Smoothie

The honeydew melon, papaya/pawpaw, and orange juice are all loaded with the vitamins and minerals needed to keep your immune system strong. The cucumber contains natural diuretics which help flush impurities out of your system, while the hemp seeds contain a near perfect balance of omega – 3 to omega – 6 fatty acids.

Yields: 2 Servings

Ingredients:

- 2-4 handfuls chopped romaine lettuce
- 170g honeydew melon – chopped
- 145g papaya/pawpaw – chopped
- ½ large cucumber
- 240ml fresh orange juice
- 2 tablespoons hemp seeds

Directions:

1. Throw all the ingredients into your NutriBullet and blitz until smooth.
2. Pour and garnish with a slice of cucumber.
3. Imbibe and live longer!

Health Benefits:

- ✓ Very high in vitamin B6 and C
- ✓ Very high in phosphorus
- ✓ High in magnesium and potassium
- ✓ Very low in sodium
- ✓ Low in saturated fat
- ✓ Cholesterol free!

Nutritional values per serving: Calories: 193; Total Fat: 5.4g; Cholesterol: 0mg; Sodium: 27mg; Potassium: 762mg; Carbohydrates: 33.5g; Protein: 6.1g

Weight Loss Smoothies

Most of us have nothing short of a love/hate relationship with dieting and calories. We all know that restricting our calories to a point is necessary, but few of us enjoy the deprivation that comes hand in hand with being able to fit into your skinny jeans comfortably.

Snacking between meals is more often than not the death knell of even the most well-meaning of dieter's intentions to stay on the straight and narrow. Most of us are capable of sticking to healthy food at mealtimes, but few of us can resist the rumblings and grumblings of hunger pangs that strike mid-afternoon and this is where most diets are derailed in the blink of an eye. Sitting in your office, feeling faint from hunger (healthy salad lunches don't go far!) you visit the bathroom which happens to be situated next to the office vending machine and before you know it, you are inhaling a candy bar, then spending the rest of the afternoon cocooned in guilt and self-loathing for once again succumbing to your weak resolve.

So what's the answer then? .... Why not smoothies?

They tick all the boxes:

- ✓ They can be made to be a complete meal in a glass
- ✓ They are literally bursting with nutrition
- ✓ They are easy to make and taste yummy to boot!
- ✓ They are naturally low in calories (when made properly).

Simply by making a few easy substitutions to good old faithful personal favorites, you can drop the calorie count without changing the taste dramatically. Sound good? Read on...

Good old H2O is the answer to most of your calorie related problems. If your jeans are feeling a little snug simply forgo juices, milks, yoghurts and the like and blend up your smoothie with water instead – that cuts out a WHACK of calories. Stick to what is deemed 'negative calorie' fruits and veggies. Things where the calorie count is less than what your body will utilize to burn it up – apples, cucumber, and watermelon are good choices here.

And lastly if you absolutely cannot stomach a smoothie without added sweetness, your best bet is to add a little Stevia. Stevia has zero sugar and zero calories, but is up to 300 times sweeter than regular table sugar. This South American herb has no effect on your blood sugar levels making it the ideal choice to sweeten up your smoothies when you are trying to lose weight.

And that's it folks – getting yourself in shape has never been easier with this selection of smoothies that all come in under 200 calories per serving! So get these low calorie smoothies down and look forward to a bikini summer!

Watermelon Lime Smoothie

This delicious smoothie may be super low in calories but it is not deficient in nutrition. It contains high dosages of vitamins to energize you and fiber and protein to keep you full for longer. Fiber also plays a role in keeping your digestive system regular which over time speeds up your metabolism and keeps you burning the calories you consume at a steady pace!

Yields: 2 Servings

Ingredients:

- 1-2 handfuls of kale
- 330g frozen watermelon
- 1 green apple
- 1 frozen banana
- Juice of ½ lime
- 60ml water if needed

Directions:

1. Throw all the ingredients into your NutriBullet and blitz until smooth.
2. Consume and feel thinner!

Health Benefits:

- ✓ Very high in vitamins A, B6, and C
- ✓ High in manganese and potassium
- ✓ High in dietary fiber
- ✓ Low in sodium
- ✓ Very low in saturated fat
- ✓ Cholesterol free!

Nutritional values per serving: Calories: 183; Total Fat: 0.2g; Cholesterol: 0mg; Sodium: 32mg; Potassium: 807mg; Carbohydrates: 44.4g; Protein: 3.5g

Grapefruit Surprise Smoothie

The surprise in this smoothie is how yummy it is! The flavor of the grapefruit is there but the sweetness of the other fruits covers the usual bitterness associated with this fruit. The potassium in this smoothie helps maintain an ideal fluid salt balance thus preventing water retention and the accompanying bloat, leaving you feeling slim and trim.

Yields: 2 Servings

Ingredients:

- 1-2 handfuls Swiss chard
- 1 frozen banana
- 230g grapefruit
- 2 kiwi fruit
- 1 orange
- Stevia to taste
- Water to max line

Directions:

1. Combine all the ingredients in your NutriBullet and blitz until smooth.
2. Garnish with twisty/bendy straws and a slice of orange.
3. Drink and enjoy!

Health Benefits:

- ✓ Very high in vitamins A, B6, and C
- ✓ High in dietary fiber
- ✓ High in potassium and magnesium
- ✓ Low in sodium
- ✓ Very low in saturated fat
- ✓ Cholesterol Free!

Nutritional values per serving: Calories: 186; Total Fats: 0.7g; Cholesterol: 0mg; Sodium: 80mg; Potassium: 911mg; Carbohydrates: 46g; Protein: 3.7g

Triple Berry Bomber

This smoothie is the bomb dude! It is high in dietary fiber and vitamins, low in calories, and tastes awesome too! Plus the goji berries in this smoothie really help to facilitate weight loss. So enjoy the bomb of antioxidants bombarding your system as you sip on this delicious smoothie.

Yields: 2 Servings

Ingredients:

- 1-2 handfuls of kale
- 1 apple, cored
- 72g blackberries
- 65g raspberries
- 28g organic goji berries
- 1 sprig of mint
- Stevia to taste (optional)
- Water to max line

Directions:

1. Rinse the berries and place them in the NutriBullet with the other ingredients and blitz until smooth.
2. Pour, add a straw, and sip!

Health Benefits:

- ✓ Very high in vitamins A, B6, and C
- ✓ Very high in manganese and iron
- ✓ Very high in dietary fiber
- ✓ Very low in sodium
- ✓ Very low in saturated fats
- ✓ Cholesterol Free!

Nutritional values per serving: Calories: 161; Total Fats: 1g; Cholesterol: 0mg; Sodium: 30mg; Potassium: 531mg; Carbohydrates: 36.6g; Protein: 3.3g

The Broc Lesner Smoothie

Broccoli is rich in potassium which is beneficial to the nervous system as it helps to carry oxygen to our brains. It also contains two phytonutrient antioxidants, zeaxanthin and lutein. These are the only two carotenoids found in the lens and the retina, so eating broccoli promotes healthy eyesight by preventing free radical damage in those areas. This is a bomb of health benefits without the calories – what more could you ask for?

Yields: 2 Servings

Ingredients:

- 50g frozen broccoli
- 1 frozen banana
- ½ large peach
- 120ml 100% pomegranate juice
- Water to max line

Directions:

1. Place all the ingredients into the NutriBullet and fire it up for 30 to 60 seconds.
2. Sip and grow strong while feeling the pounds melt away!

Health Benefits:

- ✓ Very high in vitamins B6 and C
- ✓ High in potassium
- ✓ High in dietary fiber
- ✓ Very low in sodium
- ✓ Very low in saturated fat
- ✓ Cholesterol free!

Nutritional values per serving: Calories: 113; Total Fat: 0.2g; Cholesterol: 0mg; Sodium: 11mg; Potassium: 508mg; Carbohydrates: 28g; Protein: 1.6g

The Oats So Easy Smoothie

What a great way to start your day! The delicious flavors of oats and honey combined with a small caffeine kick and nutrients from the berries makes this the breakfast of champions! The oats will keep you feeling full until lunch, the green tea energizes you for the day ahead, while the fruits nourish the body.

Yields: 2 Servings

Ingredients:

- 40g oats
- 1 apple, cored
- 150g mixed berries
- 135ml fat free Greek yoghurt
- Ice as needed
- stevia to taste
- 360ml green tea

Directions:

1. Pour steaming hot water into a glass and add 2 green tea bags. Allow to brew for 3 minutes. Remove tea bags, add stevia, and stir. Let tea cool to room temperature.
2. Sip this yummy smoothie and kick back!

Health Benefits:

- ✓ High in Vitamin B6 and C
- ✓ High in manganese
- ✓ High in dietary fiber
- ✓ Low in sodium
- ✓ Very low in saturated fat
- ✓ Cholesterol free!

Nutritional values per serving: Calories: 163; Total Fat: 1.2g; Cholesterol: 0mg; Sodium: 47mg; Potassium: 190mg; Carbohydrates: 33.5g; Protein: 7.1g

The Blues Brother Smoothie

This is the ideal low calorie smoothie to have prior to a workout session or if you have a busy day ahead. It is low in calories but still has a healthy amount of good fats and dietary fiber to give you a sustained release of energy. This will minimize the 'crash and burn' feeling often associated with calorie restricted diets by keeping you full for longer.

Yields: 2 Servings

Ingredients:

- 1-2 handfuls of spinach
- ½ frozen banana
- 150g blueberries
- ½ avocado, pitted and peeled
- dash of vanilla extract
- stevia to taste
- water to max line

Directions:

1. Pour all the ingredients into your NutriBullet and blast them until smooth.
2. Garnish with twisty/ bendy straws and a cocktail umbrella.
3. Drink up and get healthy and fit.

Health Benefits:

- ✓ Very high in vitamins A, B6, and C
- ✓ Very low in sodium
- ✓ High in dietary fiber
- ✓ High in manganese
- ✓ Cholesterol free!

Nutritional values per serving: Calories: 183; Total Fat: 10.2g; Cholesterol: 0mg; Sodium: 28mg; Potassium: 576mg; Carbohydrates: 22.9g; Protein: 2.6g

Kiwi Lime Smoothie

This is a great post workout or mid afternoon snack smoothie. Most of the calories are from natural sugars which your body needs after exercise or a long day to give you an energy boost. Because the sugars are natural you will avoid the insulin spike and subsequent crash afterwards because your body will process them at a slower rate. Make this a green smoothie if you'd like by adding a small handful of spinach.

Yields: 2 Servings

Ingredients:

- 3 kiwis, peeled and halved
- 1 pear
- 1 frozen banana
- juice from 1 lime
- ½ teaspoon vanilla extract
- 120ml water
- stevia to taste

Directions:

1. Toss all the ingredients into your NutriBullet and power it up until smooth.
2. Garnish with a twisty/bendy straw and some kiwi.
3. Enjoy feeling refreshed!

Health Benefits:

- ✓ Very high in vitamins B6 and C
- ✓ High in dietary fiber
- ✓ High in potassium
- ✓ Very low in saturated fat
- ✓ Very low in sodium
- ✓ Cholesterol free!

Nutritional values per serving: Calories: 165; Total Fat: 0.7g; Cholesterol: 0mg; Sodium: 5mg; Potassium: 651mg; Carbohydrates: 41g; Protein: 2.1g

Berry Smooth Apple Smoothie

This delicious ultra-low calorie smoothie is a must for those of us trying to lose weight and remain healthy. It is packed with vitamins and fiber whilst being super low in fats. A guilt free snack to enjoy between meals!

Yields: 2 Servings

Ingredients:

- 1-2 handfuls spinach
- 1 large apple, cored
- 150g blueberries
- 4 strawberries
- 1 tablespoon hemp seeds
- ice as needed
- water to max line

Directions:

1. Toss all the ingredients into your NutriBullet and power it up until smooth.
2. Garnish with a twisty/bendy straw and some fruit.
3. Sip and enjoy!

Health benefits:

- ✓ Very high in vitamins A, B6, and C
- ✓ Very high in magnesium and
- ✓ High in dietary fiber
- ✓ Very low in sodium
- ✓ Very low in saturated fats
- ✓ Cholesterol Free!

Nutritional values per serving: Calories: 146; Total Fats: 2.8g; Cholesterol: 0mg; Sodium: 26mg; Potassium: 398mg; Carbohydrates 30.1g; Protein: 3.5g

Cucumber Splash Smoothie

Most people don't consume enough liquids. This, in severe situations, can lead to many dangerous conditions such as irregular heart beat and/or mental impairment. Constant mild dehydration puts a strain on your kidneys and many other organs because of a buildup of toxins in the body. All the ingredients in this smoothie have great rehydration properties and its super low in calories!

Yields: 2 Servings

Ingredients:

- 4 kale leaves
- ½ large cucumber
- 640g watermelon
- 8 frozen strawberries
- Juice from 1 lime
- Small handful fresh mint leaves
- Stevia to taste

Directions:

1. Combine all the ingredients in your NutriBullet and blitz until smooth.
2. Drink and feel hydrated!

Health Benefits:

- ✓ Very high in vitamins A and C
- ✓ High in potassium and iron
- ✓ High in dietary fiber
- ✓ Very low in sodium
- ✓ Low in saturated fat
- ✓ Cholesterol Free!

Nutritional values per serving: Calories: 146; Total Fat: 0.8g; Cholesterol: 0mg; Sodium: 17mg; Potassium: 693mg; Carbohydrates: 33.8g; Protein: 3.6g

Green Mango Citrus Smoothie

Parsley is derived from a Greek word for 'rock celery' and like celery it is packed with loads of vitamins, minerals, fiber, and phytochemicals. The orange, banana, and spinach also contain these beneficial substances and they taste better too! Citrus and most especially lemon has traditionally been associated with weight loss and fat burning.

Yields: 2 Servings

Ingredients:

- 15g chopped parsley
- 1 handful of spinach
- 1 orange, peeled
- 165g mango – chopped
- 1 frozen banana
- 1 tbsp. lemon juice
- Stevia to taste
- Water to max line

Directions:

1. Place all the ingredients into the NutriBullet and blaze away until smooth.
2. Suck down your citrus smoothie!

Health Benefits:

- ✓ Very high in vitamins A, B6, and C
- ✓ High in potassium
- ✓ High in dietary fiber
- ✓ Very low in sodium
- ✓ Very low in saturated fat
- ✓ Cholesterol Free!

Nutritional values per serving: Calories: 156; Total Fat: 0.5g; Cholesterol: 0mg; Sodium: 19mg; Potassium: 664mg; Carbohydrates: 42.9g; Protein: 2.6g

Romaine Rock star Smoothie

Romaine lettuce is a mineral rich rock star! The wide variety of nutrients that Romaine lettuce provides, including iron, protein, calcium, vitamin A and Omega-3s are *hugely* beneficial to your health making this the perfect ingredient to include in any low calorie smoothie. Best of all, it has a very mild flavor that is easy to hide in smoothies. You can literally add a whole head of Romaine lettuce into you smoothie and barely know it's there. Drink up and rock out!

Yields: 2 Servings

Ingredients:

- 2-4 handfuls chopped Romaine lettuce
- 1 apple, cored
- 165g mango – chopped
- 72g blackberries
- 180g pineapple
- ice as needed
- water to max line

Directions:

1. Place all the ingredients into the NutriBullet and fire it up until smooth.
2. Slurp down this delicious healthy smoothie.

Health Benefits:

- ✓ Very high in vitamins B6 and C
- ✓ High in dietary fiber
- ✓ Very low in sodium
- ✓ Very low in saturated fat
- ✓ Cholesterol Free!

Nutritional values per serving: Calories: 161; Total Fat: 0.5g; Cholesterol: 0mg; Sodium: 6mg; Potassium: 401mg; Carbohydrates: 37g; Protein: 1.4g

Gaga for Goji Smoothie

Goji berries have a glycemic index rating of only 29 out of 100. What this means is that they are more likely to satisfy your hunger and cravings than increase them compared to high GI foods. So they help to turn your regular smoothie into a meal replacement. They also provide a boost of energy, promote healthy skin, protect the eyes, and are jam-packed with fiber which helps to manage weight. Did I mention that they are the most nutritionally dense fruit on Earth?! Go goji go!

Yields: 2 Servings

Ingredients:

- 3 tablespoons goji berries
- 1-2 handfuls of spinach
- 1 frozen banana
- 1 apple
- 50g cranberries
- Coconut water to max line

Directions:

1. Add the ingredients into the NutriBullet and blitz away until smooth.
2. Drink and revitalize!

Health Benefits:

- ✓ Very high in vitamins A, B6 and C
- ✓ High in potassium
- ✓ High in manganese
- ✓ Very low in sodium
- ✓ Very low in saturated fat
- ✓ Cholesterol Free!

Nutritional values per serving: Calories: 193; Total Fat: 1.1g; Cholesterol: 0mg; Sodium: 215mg; Potassium: 946mg; Carbohydrates: 45.2g; Protein: 3.2g

Peach Watermelon Blast Smoothie

Here is a smoothie that incorporates all the best qualities that you want in a low calorie smoothie. Firstly it is very low in calories and secondly it is highly nutritious, it also has hydrating qualities and it is rich in fiber! This will top your lists of favorites after the first sip!

Yields: 2 Servings

Ingredients:

- 1-2 handfuls of kale
- 1 peach, pitted
- 495g frozen watermelon
- 5 strawberries
- Juice of ½ lemon
- 60ml water if needed

Directions:

1. Throw all the ingredients into your NutriBullet and blitz until smooth.
2. Consume and enjoy all the benefits!

Health Benefits:

- ✓ Very high in vitamins A, B6, and C
- ✓ Very high in manganese
- ✓ High in potassium and magnesium
- ✓ Low in sodium
- ✓ Very low in saturated fat
- ✓ Cholesterol free!

Nutritional values per serving: Calories: 134; Total Fat: 0.5g; Cholesterol: 0mg; Sodium: 32mg; Potassium: 721mg; Carbohydrates: 31.1g; Protein: 4g

The Dandelion Smoothie

Dandelion greens have many great qualities, they are mildly diuretic thus aiding in weight loss. They are also loaded with vitamin A, E, and K and many minerals and phytochemicals. Plus they have anti-inflammatory properties and are considered to be prebiotics. All this means that this is a nutritionally sound smoothie without the calories – the best kind!

Yields: 2 Servings

Ingredients:

- 1 handful dandelion greens
- 165g mango
- 1 frozen banana
- 4 strawberries
- 1 orange, peeled
- Water to max line

Directions:

1. Combine all the ingredients in your NutriBullet and blitz until smooth.
2. Garnish with twisty/bendy straws and a slice of cucumber.
3. Drink and enjoy!

Health Benefits:

- ✓ Very high in vitamins A, B6, and C
- ✓ High in potassium
- ✓ High in dietary fiber
- ✓ Very low in sodium
- ✓ Very low in saturated fat
- ✓ Cholesterol free!

Nutritional values per serving; Calories: 165; Total Fat: 0.5g; Cholesterol: 0mg; Sodium: 12mg; Potassium: 565mg; Carbohydrates: 36.8g; Protein: 2.3g

Protein & 'Dessert' Smoothies

Word is out – you don't have to be a ravenous carnivore that devours rare steak at every meal to get your daily quota of protein anymore. In fact, you don't even have to eat meat at all if you don't want to! Protein is one of the 4 essential macro nutrients that the human body needs to survive – the others are carbohydrates, fats and water. So protein is very important if we want our bodies to work properly.

Most people erroneously think that protein is just for bulging muscled body builders, but research has shown that protein is one of the most essential building blocks of the body. It supports strong and healthy hair, nails, skin, bones and muscles. It is also an essential component in weight control as it helps to keep you feeling full for longer. Making sure there is enough protein consumed at each meal, will help to prevent the between meal snacking that is often responsible for the derailment of a healthy lifestyle.

Now that is not to say that we need loads of protein to be healthy. You will be surprised to learn that we actually need very little protein daily to meet our body's demands. An adult over the age of 18 only needs 0.36g of protein per pound that they weigh, per day to get enough in their diet. For a person of average weight, that can be as little as around 50g of protein per day. Smoothies are a super easy and portable source of protein and an easy way to meet your daily protein requirements; especially if you are a vegetarian. They are the perfect between meal fillers and if you are training in the gym or doing sport, a protein smoothie is the perfect post workout treat to help your body and muscles recover.

The trick is to find the right sources of protein to include. Chia seeds, Greek yoghurt, flax seeds, pumpkin seeds, sunflower seeds, hemp seeds, cooked quinoa and eggs will send the protein measurements of your smoothie soaring. Nuts and nut butters are great go to options for protein, most especially almond, walnut, and peanut (providing there are no nut allergies to consider). Spirulina is a great addition if you can handle the pungent taste. Other great sources of protein include tofu, cottage cheese, coconut milk, seaweed, oats, and soy products. Whey protein powders also pack a protein whammy and can be added to any smoothie to up the protein content. Unfortunately, most whey proteins are *highly* processed options. So if you're going to use whey protein powder please ensure that it is cold-processed organic whey powder free of artificial sweeteners.

And finally, if you are still at a loss, remember that cacao nibs contain a whopping 4 grams of protein in every ounce! Kind of makes you wonder why I bothered to write about anything else, doesn't it?

Note: Most of the recipes in this section (and in this book) serve 2, so be careful. If you do drink both servings you will get double the protein, but also double the calories.

Oatmeal Raisin Cookie Smoothie

This yummy smoothie is a great breakfast or snack and it tastes like dessert! The oats digest slowly and will give you a sustained energy release throughout the morning, while the raisins, and banana provide a variety of vitamins and a healthy kick of energy. If you don't have organic protein powder available, but you still need to increase your protein, add 135ml of Greek yoghurt instead. There are also vegan versions of vanilla protein powder. Either way, you can't lose with this smoothie.

Yields: 2 Servings

Ingredients:

- 40g rolled oats
- 1 frozen banana
- 1 tbsp. almond butter (or any nut butter)
- 1 teaspoon vanilla extract
- ½ tsp. ground cinnamon
- dash of nutmeg
- 37g raisins (optional)
- 1 scoop organic vanilla whey powder
- 240ml unsweetened vanilla almond milk

Directions:

1. Combine all the ingredients in your NutriBullet and blitz until smooth.
2. Drink and enjoy!

Health Benefits:

- ✓ Very high in protein
- ✓ Low in saturated fat
- ✓ High in manganese
- ✓ High in calcium

Nutritional values per serving: Calories: 280; Total Fat: 7.6g; Cholesterol: 25mg; Sodium: 153mg; Potassium: 623mg; Carbohydrates: 39.5g; Protein: 15.2g

Apple Peanut Butter Smoothie

We all know that apples and peanut butter go well together and this smoothie is no exception. It's delicious! This is a great smoothie for those pushing themselves hard in the gym. It is relatively high in protein, calories, and carbohydrates. This will provide you with sufficient energy to work out without fearing that you will burn out and 'hit the wall'. Add some raw cacao powder and a little honey if you'd like and make this smoothie even more wonderful.

Yields: 1 Large Serving

Ingredients:

- 1 handful of kale
- 2 apples
- 2 tablespoons peanut butter
- 40g oats
- ¼ tsp cinnamon
- Unsweetened almond milk to max line

Directions:

1. Toss all the ingredients into your NutriBullet and power it up until smooth.
2. Pour it into a cup and garnish with a twisty/bendy straw and some fruit.
3. Sip and enjoy!

Health Benefits:

- ✓ Very high in protein
- ✓ Very high in vitamins A, B6, and C
- ✓ High in manganese
- ✓ High in calcium and dietary fiber
- ✓ Low in saturated fat
- ✓ Cholesterol free!

Nutritional values per serving: Calories: 563; Total Fat: 24.4g; Cholesterol: 0mg; Sodium: 394mg; Potassium: 1375mg; Carbohydrates: 78.8g; Protein: 13.5g

Pumpkin Pie Smoothie

During the fall, I go a little pumpkin crazy. Yes, I am a lover of all things pumpkin and this Halloween smoothie does not disappoint! Creamy, filling, and fabulous! If you don't have hemp seeds on hand, just add 135ml of fat free Greek yoghurt and that will provide over 10 grams of protein. Or replace the unsweetened almond milk with soy milk and that will also do the trick. Either way, you've got to try this one!

Yields: 1 Serving

Ingredients:

- 122g Libby's pure canned pumpkin
- ½ frozen banana
- ¼ tsp vanilla
- ¼ tsp cinnamon
- Dash of nutmeg
- 180ml unsweetened almond milk
- 1 tablespoon honey
- 2 tablespoons hemp seeds
- 27g almonds, slivered

Directions:

1. Tip all the ingredients into the NutriBullet and fire away until smooth.
2. Guzzle down and grow healthy!

Health Benefits:

- ✓ Very high in protein
- ✓ Very high in vitamin A and E
- ✓ High in calcium
- ✓ Low in saturated fat
- ✓ Low in sodium
- ✓ Cholesterol free!

Nutritional values per serving: Calories: 410; Total Fat: 23.5; Cholesterol: 0mg; Sodium: 139mg; Potassium: 771mg; Carbohydrates: 45.3g; Protein: 13.9g

The Whey Out There Smoothie

Whey powder is an excellent source of high quality protein. It will also thicken up the smoothie and give it a creamier texture. (Just make sure that the whey powder you select is organic and cold processed.) The orange, apple, papaya, kiwi, and grapefruit add an incredible flavor dimension while simultaneously providing you with natural energy for your workout.

Yields: 2 Servings

Ingredients:

- 1 handful chopped dandelion greens
- 1 orange
- 1 apple
- 75g papaya/pawpaw
- 2 kiwi fruit, peeled
- 230g grapefruit
- 1 scoop organic whey powder
- Water to max line

Directions:

1. Place all the ingredients into the NutriBullet and fire it up until smooth.
2. Sip and grow strong!

Health Benefits:

- ✓ Very high in protein
- ✓ Very high in vitamin C
- ✓ High in vitamin A
- ✓ High in dietary fiber
- ✓ Low in sodium
- ✓ Low in saturated fat

Nutritional values per serving: Calories: 262; Total Fat: 1.9g; Cholesterol: 0mg; Sodium: 87mg; Potassium: 923mg; Carbohydrates: 52.3g; Protein: 13.9g

Banana Walnut Smoothie

This no-nonsense, easy to make smoothie is designed to fuel your engine for the long haul! It is comparatively high in protein, high in calories, and high in the good fats. The fats will keep you mentally alert and improve your concentration, while the protein and calories keep your muscles working properly over extended periods. This smoothie packs a powerful protein punch!

Yields: 2 Servings

Ingredients:

- 1 frozen banana
- ½ avocado, pitted and peeled
- 30g walnuts
- 2 tablespoons honey
- Dash of cinnamon
- Soy milk to max line

Directions:

1. Add the ingredients into the NutriBullet and smash away until smooth.
2. Drink and revitalize!

Health Benefits:

- ✓ Very high in protein
- ✓ High in manganese
- ✓ Very low in sodium
- ✓ No cholesterol

Nutritional values per serving: Calories: 415; Total Fat: 22.2g; Cholesterol: 0mg; Sodium: 98mg; Potassium: 766mg; Carbohydrates: 48.4g; Protein: 11.4g

The Other Whey Smoothie

This is such a delicious smoothie, and with the whey powder you feel well prepared for the day (or work-out) ahead. Whey is a complete protein source that provides your body with all the goodness you get from meat without having to eat any. This makes it an e great dietary supplement for vegetarians. Remember, if you're vegan there are all sorts of vegan protein powder varieties. Either way, be sure to buy organic!

Yields: 2 Servings

Ingredients:

- 1-2 handfuls of spinach
- 1 pear
- 180g pineapple
- 92g green grapes
- 75g blueberries
- ½ avocado
- 1 scoop whey powder
- Coconut water to max line

Directions:

1. Place all the ingredients in your NutriBullet and fire it up until smooth.
2. Sip this yummy smoothie and prepare to work-out!

Health Benefits:

- ✓ Very high in protein
- ✓ Very high in vitamin A, B6, and C
- ✓ Very high in manganese
- ✓ High in dietary fiber

Nutritional values per serving: Calories: 325; Total Fat: 11.6g; Cholesterol: 25mg; Sodium: 216mg; Potassium: 1087mg; Carbohydrates: 46.6g; Protein: 14.4g

Peanut Butter & Jelly Smoothie

I'm pretty sure that no one else consumed as much peanut butter and jelly sandwiches as I did when I was a child. I still enjoy them to this day and my kids have carried on the tradition. So this smoothie is a favorite in my home. Thanks to the delicious oats and peanut butter it's also very filling and a great source of protein too. Winner!

Yields: 1 Serving

Ingredients:

- 4 frozen strawberries
- 40g dry oats
- ½ frozen banana
- 2 tablespoons natural peanut butter
- 1-2 tablespoons natural jam
- 120ml unsweetened almond milk
- A bit of stevia

Directions:

1. Pour all the ingredients into your NutriBullet and blast them until smooth.
2. Drink up and get healthy and strong!

Health Benefits:

- ✓ Very high in protein
- ✓ Very high in vitamins B6 and C
- ✓ High in manganese
- ✓ Cholesterol free!

Nutritional values per serving: Calories: 404; Total Fat: 18.8g; Cholesterol: 0mg; Sodium: 246mg; Potassium: 667mg; Carbohydrates: 51.5g; Protein: 12.2g

Yummy Egg Nog Smoothie

This smoothie is a staple in my home and usually in heavy rotation since I always have all of the ingredients on hand. Don't let the raw eggs in the smoothie throw you off. It is AMAZING and yes, it tastes just like egg nog. And thanks to the eggs and almonds in this smoothie it is a wonderful source of protein! This smoothie is also very delicious with coconut milk instead of almond.

Yields: 2 Servings

Ingredients:

- 4 raw eggs (pastured or organic)
- 240ml unsweetened almond milk
- 1 frozen banana
- 1 tsp cinnamon
- 2 tsps. vanilla extract
- ¼ tsp of nutmeg
- 1 tablespoon honey
- 27g slivered almonds (optional)

Directions:

1. Combine all the ingredients in your NutriBullet and blitz until smooth.
2. Drink and get healthy from all the vitamins!

Health Benefits:

- ✓ Very high in protein
- ✓ High in calcium
- ✓ High in selenium
- ✓ High in vitamin E

Nutritional values per serving: Calories: 310; Total Fat: 16.1g; Cholesterol: 327mg; Sodium: 215mg; Potassium: 519mg; Carbohydrates: 27.4g; Protein: 14.8g

Apple Carrot Coconut Smoothie

Usually when you see a smoothie with seeds in it you think about picking the seed bits out of your teeth after drinking it. With the NutriBullet you will never have that problem again. The motor is so powerful and the blades so well designed that all ingredients are smashed to a powder or a paste. You therefore are able to get all the ingredients down and digest them more completely than ever before.

Yields: 2 Servings

Ingredients:

- 2-4 handfuls of spinach
- 1 apple
- 1 whole carrot
- 1 frozen banana
- 1 tablespoon coconut oil
- ½ tablespoon freshly grated ginger
- Dash of cinnamon
- 16g pumpkin seeds
- Soy milk to max line

Directions:

1. Throw all the ingredients into your NutriBullet and blitz until smooth.
2. Consume and feel rejuvenated!

Health Benefits:

- ✓ Very high in protein
- ✓ Very high in vitamins A, B6, and C
- ✓ Low in sodium
- ✓ High in magnesium
- ✓ High in manganese
- ✓ Cholesterol free!

Nutritional values per serving: Calories: 350; Total Fat: 17.2g; Cholesterol: 0mg; Sodium: 136mg; Potassium: 1044mg; Carbohydrates: 43.1g; Protein: 10.9g

Cleanse and Detox Smoothies

If you think of your digestive system like a pool pump, it becomes really easy to understand how it all works. The creepy crawly sucks up the dirt, passes it through a filter and eliminates all the debris, leaving your pool sparkly, shiny and clean. To maintain this system, it is necessary to clean out the filter and add chemicals to the water. If you don't clean out the filter, it becomes incapable of doing its job properly and instead of being eliminated, the debris finds its way back into the pool. Your water is dirty and a bright shade of algae green and nobody wants to put so much as their pinky toe into it!

In much the same way, you need to keep your liver and kidneys, the body's filtration system, clean if you want them to work properly. We are living in a world that is becoming more and more plagued by toxins. We get far more than we should through our food, our drinking water is full of chemicals and the air we breathe at times is just plain disgusting. All this debris has to go somewhere and unfortunately it passes through our system and settles in our digestive tract. Now, biologically speaking, we were designed pretty well, but unfortunately our systems just can't evolve fast enough to keep up with our rapid developments in other areas. Compared to even just 50 years ago, the amount of toxins we are being exposed to has reached epidemic proportions and while our body is naturally geared towards toxic elimination, every so often it needs a bit of a helping hand to handle the sheer volume that we are being bombarded with.

Just as we would clean out the pool filter, we need to clean out our body's filter and that means going on a detox. Now I'm not talking about all the drastic liquid fasts and starvation diets that are currently sweeping the world. I'm talking about putting wholesome things into your body that assist, aid and accelerate the process of cleansing to help detoxify your body from the buildup of harmful substances in your digestive system. Failure to do this will result in a sluggish digestive system that cannot do its job properly.

Luckily, the solution is a no-brainer! Something as simple as drinking detox smoothies on a regular basis can eliminate all these problems. A properly functioning digestive system is crucial to good health and it doesn't get easier or quicker than simply sipping on one of these delicious smoothies a couple times a week. And what better way to do this than with ingredients such as acai berries, goji berries, coconut water, pomegranates, lemons, cucumbers, cranberries, blueberries, apples, beets, turmeric, garlic, ginger, cayenne pepper, cilantro, parsley, mint, cinnamon and green tea. Include one or more of these ingredients to the following basic smoothie recipes and really feel the difference – clean on the inside, healthy on the outside!

Even if you don't believe in detoxing, you have nothing to lose, so don't waste another minute – fire up the NutriBullet and whip up one of these amazing smoothies.

Refreshing Romaine Smoothie

The Romaine lettuce and the strawberries are high in fiber. This binds to free radicals and along with the coconut water, apple, lemon, and flax seeds helps to flush out all the unwanted toxins from our bodies. This refreshing smoothie will have you feeling purged of all toxic waste in no time!

Yields: 2 Servings

Ingredients:

- 2-4 handfuls chopped Romaine lettuce
- 2 apples
- 6 strawberries
- Juice of ½ lemon
- 2 tablespoons flax seeds
- Coconut water to max line

Directions:

1. Combine all the ingredients in your NutriBullet and blitz until smooth.
2. Pour out the smoothie into two suitable cups and garnish with twisty/bendy straws and a sliced strawberry.
3. Drink and enjoy!

Health Benefits:

- ✓ Very high in vitamins B6 and C
- ✓ Very high in dietary fiber
- ✓ High in potassium and magnesium
- ✓ High in dietary fiber
- ✓ Low in saturated fat
- ✓ Cholesterol free!

Nutritional values per serving: Calories: 204; Total Fat: 3g; Cholesterol: 0mg; Sodium: 262mg; Potassium: 1062mg; Carbohydrates: 42.1g; Protein: 3.8g

Berry Pomegranate Smoothie

Pomegranate contains very high levels of antioxidants. This is very important when detoxing as the toxins released can put your immune system under pressure, and the last thing you want is to get sick! Antioxidants also protect your body from free radical damage, which is thought to be one of the leading causes of cancer, keeping you healthy for longer.

Yields: 2 Servings

Ingredients:

- 1-2 handfuls of spinach
- 1 apple
- 240ml pure pomegranate juice
- 65g frozen raspberries
- 75g blueberries
- Water to max line

Directions:

1. Toss all the ingredients into your NutriBullet and power it up until smooth.
2. Enjoy!

Health Benefits:

- ✓ Very high in vitamins A, B6, and C
- ✓ High in potassium
- ✓ High in dietary fiber
- ✓ Low in sodium
- ✓ Very low in saturated fat
- ✓ Cholesterol free!

Nutritional values per serving: Calories: 166; Total Fat: 0.5g; Cholesterol: 0mg; Sodium: 30mg; Potassium: 639mg; Carbohydrates: 41.1g; Protein: 1.5g

Citrus Lemocado Smoothie

Avocadoes are high in fats, however the fats they contain are 'good fats' as they help with the omega – 3 to omega – 6 balance. The fat is also essential to detoxing as it stimulates the liver to produce bile which helps flush the liver. A healthy liver is essential to a healthy body as it is then able to better handle and process any toxic substances.

Yields: 2 Servings

Ingredients:

- 1-2 handfuls of kale
- 1 frozen banana
- 1 grapefruit, peeled
- 1 orange, peeled
- ½ avocado – pitted and peeled
- Juice of ½ lemon
- Water to max line

Directions:

1. Combine all the ingredients in your NutriBullet and blitz until smooth.
2. Drink and get healthy from all the vitamins!

Health Benefits:

- ✓ Very high in vitamin A, B6, and C
- ✓ High in dietary fiber
- ✓ High in manganese
- ✓ High in potassium
- ✓ Very low in sodium
- ✓ Cholesterol free!

Nutritional values per serving: Calories: 256; Total Fat: 10g; Cholesterol: 0mg; Sodium: 33mg; Potassium: 1039mg; Carbohydrates: 40.7g; Protein: 4.8g

The Q-cumba Smoothie

Cucumbers contain a wide variety of vitamins and phytochemicals which aid the body's immune system while detoxing. It also has a high water content which along with the liquids from the other ingredients, help flush the toxins out of your body. Keeping adequately hydrated is very important during the detox process and this smoothie effectively hydrates and nourishes.

Yields: 2 Servings

Ingredients:

- 1 apple
- 92g green grapes
- ½ large cucumber
- 8g cilantro
- Juice of ½ lemon
- 1" of grated ginger
- ¼ teaspoon ground cinnamon
- 240ml water
- Few ice cubes

Directions:

1. Tip all the ingredients into the NutriBullet and fire away until smooth.
2. Guzzle down and grow healthy!

Health Benefits:

- ✓ Very high in vitamins B6 and C
- ✓ Very high in manganese
- ✓ High in dietary fiber
- ✓ Very low in sodium
- ✓ Very low in saturated fat
- ✓ Cholesterol free!

Nutritional values per serving: Calories: 101; Total Fat: 0.4g; Cholesterol: 0mg; Sodium: 6mg; Potassium: 354mg; Carbohydrates: 25.5g; Protein: 1.1g

Mint Dandelion Smoothie

Mint aids in the digestion of fats and thus helps the flow of bile from the liver to the gallbladder. It also has properties which help the muscles of the intestines relax when cramping. This is an incredibly refreshing and wonderfully nutritious smoothie to enjoy while detoxing.

Yields: 2 Servings

Ingredients:

- 1 handful spinach
- 1 handful of dandelion greens
- 1 pear
- 1 kiwi fruit
- 90g fresh or frozen pineapple
- 1 frozen banana
- Juice of ½ lemon
- Small handful fresh mint leaves
- Water to max line

Directions:

1. Place all the ingredients into the NutriBullet and blaze away until smooth.
2. Garnish with an umbrella and a twisty/bendy straw.
3. Suck down your minty smoothie!

Health Benefits:

- ✓ Very high in vitamins A, B6, and C
- ✓ Very high in manganese
- ✓ High in iron
- ✓ Very low in saturated fat
- ✓ Low in sodium
- ✓ Cholesterol free!

Nutritional values per serving:; Calories: 157; Total Fat: 0.7g; Cholesterol: 0mg; Sodium: 39mg; Potassium: 703mg; Carbohydrates: 39.2g; Protein: 3g

The Beetox Smoothie

Beets contain a substance called betalain which is a powerful antioxidant, fungicidal and anti-inflammatory. This makes it ideal for detoxing as it will support the bodies healing process and disease fighting capability, building immunity while flushing all the waste – the perfect disease fighting combo.

Yields: 2 Servings

Ingredients:

- 1 small beet – steamed to soften
- 8 frozen strawberries
- 78g cherries, pits removed
- 1 orange, peeled
- 240ml coconut water
- Ice as needed

Directions:

1. Place all the ingredients into the NutriBullet and fire it up until smooth.
2. Sip and grow strong!

Health Benefits:

- ✓ Very high in vitamin C
- ✓ High in manganese
- ✓ Very high in dietary fiber
- ✓ High in potassium
- ✓ Low in saturated fat
- ✓ Cholesterol free!

Nutritional values per serving: Calories: 147; Total Fat: 0.6g; Cholesterol: 0mg; Sodium: 172mg; Potassium: 732mg; Carbohydrates: 34.4g; Protein: 3g

Strawberry Mint Smoothie

This delicious strawberry cucumber mint smoothie is *sooo* refreshing, creamy, and light. Perfect for a hot summer day. Even my 4 year old loves it! Besides being delicious, the strawberries help to cleanse while the cucumber helps to eliminate toxins. Cucumbers also contain minerals that are beneficial to our skin, namely, potassium, magnesium, calcium, folate and silicon. An all-round nutrition boost that tastes scrumptious! Add a piece of kiwi to jazz this up even more if you'd like!

Yields: 1 Serving

Ingredients:

- 12 frozen strawberries
- ½ large cucumber -- peeled and chopped
- 5 mint leaves
- Squeeze of lemon
- 240ml unsweetened almond milk
- Stevia to taste

Directions:

4. Toss all the ingredients into your NutriBullet and power it up until smooth.
5. Pour and garnish with a twisty/bendy straw and some fruit.
6. Enjoy!

Health Benefits:

- ✓ Very high in vitamins A, C, and E
- ✓ Very high in calcium
- ✓ High in manganese, potassium, and magnesium
- ✓ High in iron and dietary fiber
- ✓ Very low in saturated fat
- ✓ Cholesterol free!

Nutritional values per serving: Calories: 127; Total Fat: 3.4g; Cholesterol: 0mg; Sodium: 189mg; Potassium: 774mg; Carbohydrates: 24g; Protein: 3.8g

The De-stress Me Smoothie

This delicious smoothie helps you to relax, de-stress, and even sleep better due to the carefully selected ingredients. The spinach and basil are high in magnesium which helps the muscles and nerves to relax, the kiwi and orange are high in vitamin C which has been proven to reduce anxiety, and the green tea contains catechins which reduces stress throughout your body. All of the ingredients help to calm you and provide valuable nutrition while detoxing. What more could you ask for?

Yields: 2 Servings

Ingredients:

- 1-2 handfuls of spinach
- 1 pear
- 1 kiwi - peeled
- 1 large orange
- 5-10 fresh basil leaves
- Juice of ½ lemon
- Ice as needed
- green tea to max line

Directions:

1. Pour steaming hot water into a glass and add 2 green tea bags. Allow to brew for 3 minutes. Remove tea bags, add honey, and stir. Let tea cool to room temperature.
2. Combine all the ingredients in your NutriBullet and blitz for 30 to 60 seconds.
3. Drink up, and relax!

Health Benefits:

- ✓ Very high in vitamins A, B6, and C
- ✓ High in potassium
- ✓ Very high in dietary fiber
- ✓ Low in sodium
- ✓ Very low in saturated fats
- ✓ Cholesterol free!

Nutritional values per serving: Calories: 114; Total Fat: 0.5g; Cholesterol: 0mg; Sodium: 26mg; Potassium: 543mg; Carbohydrates: 28.3g; Protein: 2.5g

The Sprinkler Smoothie

All the ingredients in this smoothie have a high water content most especially the cucumber and the watermelon. This is important as the body needs lots of liquids when detoxing so as to flush out the toxins from our kidneys and remain hydrated. This is one delicious detox smoothie.

Yields: 1 Serving

Ingredients:

- 330g watermelon
- ½ large cucumber
- 90g fresh or frozen pineapple
- Juice of ½ lemon
- Ice as needed

Directions:

1. Place all the ingredients in your NutriBullet and fire it up until smooth.
2. Pour the contents into a cup and garnish with a twisty/bendy straw and a cucumber.
3. Sip this yummy smoothie and feel hydrated!

Health Benefits:

- ✓ Very high in vitamins A and C
- ✓ Very high in manganese
- ✓ High in potassium
- ✓ Very low in sodium
- ✓ Low in saturated fats
- ✓ Cholesterol free!

Nutritional values per serving: Calories: 155; Total Fat: 0.7g; Cholesterol: 0mg; Sodium: 8mg; Potassium: 649mg; Carbohydrates: 39.1g; Protein: 3.2g

The Heavy Metal Smoothie

Cilantro is well known for its ability to detox the body of unwanted heavy metals and other environmental toxins - this is known as chelation. Romaine lettuce has a host of vitamins, minerals and phytonutrients which will help to keep the body nourished while detoxing. The pear and papaya contain natural sugars to fuel your body with energy during this process.

Yields: 2 Servings

Ingredients:

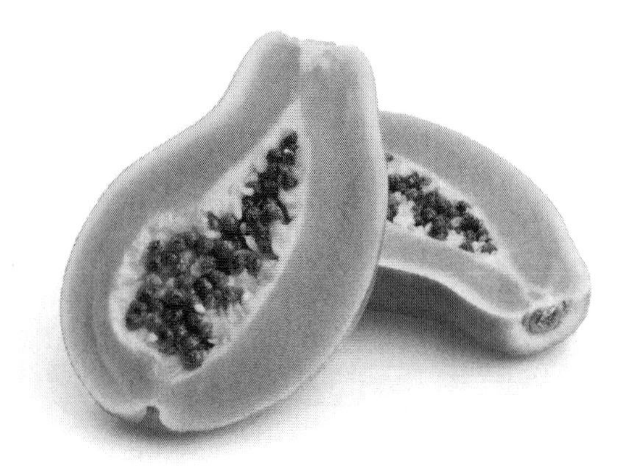

- 2-4 handfuls of chopped Romaine lettuce
- 150g papaya/pawpaw, chopped
- 1 pear
- 8g cilantro
- Coconut water to max line
- Ice as needed

Directions:

1. Throw all the ingredients into your NutriBullet and blitz until smooth.
2. Consume and feel flushed!

Health Benefits:

- ✓ Very high in vitamins A, B6 and C
- ✓ High in dietary fiber
- ✓ Very low in saturated fat
- ✓ No cholesterol

Nutritional values per serving: Calories: 133; Total Fat: 1g; Cholesterol: 0mg; Sodium: 267mg; Potassium: 991mg; Carbohydrates: 31g; Protein: 2.9g

Pineapple Cleanse Smoothie

All the ingredients in this smoothie are rich in vitamins and nutrients. The pineapple contains bromelain which helps to cleanse your colon, while the dandelions, apple, lemon, and hemp seeds filter toxins and waste from the bloodstream and keep the digestive tract clean. Super cleanse in a glass!

Yields: 2 Servings

Ingredients:

- 1 handful of dandelion greens
- 1 handful of spinach
- 1 green apple
- 180g fresh or frozen pineapple
- 92g seedless green grapes
- Juice of ½ lemon
- 1 tablespoon hemp seeds
- Coconut water to max line

Directions:

1. Combine all the ingredients in your NutriBullet and blitz until smooth.
2. Pour out the smoothie into two suitable cups and garnish with twisty/bendy straws and a slice of apple.
3. Drink and enjoy!

Health Benefits:

- ✓ Very high in vitamins A, B6, and C
- ✓ High in manganese and dietary fiber
- ✓ High in magnesium
- ✓ Very low in sodium
- ✓ Low in saturated fat
- ✓ Cholesterol free!

Nutritional values per serving: Calories: 196; Total Fat: 3.2g; Cholesterol: 0mg; Sodium: 224mg; Potassium: 978mg; Carbohydrates: 42g; Protein: 4.9g

Brain Boosting Smoothies

The brain is an often overlooked organ when it comes to dieting and health. Think about it, how many people have come to you and said "Hey, I'm going on a brain boosting diet!" That's right, probably none. This fact often baffles me and for good reason.

If you imagine your body is an army, then the brain is the general – the commander in chief. An army can only be as good as the orders it is given and accordingly your body cannot function optimally if your brain is not giving it good orders.

We live in an incredibly hectic, fast paced world where, if we are to survive, we need a brain that can process the constant barrage of stimulation that it receives. To do this our brains need to be skilled in things such as concentration, memory, clarity and focus. We also need to be able to filter out all the irrelevant stimuli we receive and pay attention only to that which is important. A tired, under-nourished brain can never do this effectively. We need to strive to ensure that our brain receives the correct doses of what it needs to do its job properly.

In addition to these vital cognitive functions, the brain also plays a role in our mood and energy levels. Depression and fatigue are two important symptoms that you should never ignore. They are indicative of a brain that is in need of some urgent TLC. By simply throwing a few key ingredients into your NutriBullet, you can recharge your brain power, boost your concentration and even stave off degenerative diseases like dementia and Alzheimer's!

Green smoothies are an excellent way to inject your brain and body with the pure nutrition it needs. Leafy greens like spinach and kale are hugely influential in the fight against Alzheimer's because they are packed full of Vitamin B6 and B12. Other great brain foods to include in your smoothies are blueberries, avocado, bananas, apple juice, goji berries, hemp seeds, kiwi fruit, chia seeds, green tea and my personal favorite – cacao! If you have ever needed an excuse to eat more chocolate, here it is folks – cacao has been shown to be a prime source of antioxidants and also increases blood flow to the brain. More blood = more oxygen = better cognition!

Mixing a smoothie requires little preparation and minimal effort, but the results are hugely beneficial to the health of our brain. Enjoy these delicious brain boosting smoothies every day to improve your overall brain function.

Pineapple Coconut Smoothie

Coconut is high in manganese, fiber, very high in medium-chain triglycerides and low in natural sugars. During periods of low blood sugar, medium-chain triglycerides are converted into a source of fuel, keeping your brain functioning at a high level, so drink this smoothie for peak performance!

Yields: 2 Servings

Ingredients:

- 180g pineapple (fresh or frozen)
- 1 frozen banana
- 240ml unsweetened coconut milk
- 1 tsp vanilla extract

Directions:

1. Add all the ingredients to your blender and blend until smooth.
2. Drink it all.
3. Enjoy the benefits!

Health benefits:

- ✓ Very high in vitamin C
- ✓ Very high in manganese
- ✓ Low in sodium
- ✓ Cholesterol Free!

Nutritional values per serving: Calories: 380; Total Fats: 29.1g; Cholesterol: 0mg; Sodium: 20mg; Potassium: 624mg; Carbohydrates: 31.3g; Protein: 3.8g

Green Mamba Smoothie

The avocado in this smoothie contains essential fatty acids omega – 3 and omega – 6 in the ideal ratio. Our brain cells are made up mostly of fats which our body cannot make itself so it is essential to eat the right fats to maximize brain function. For that reason, avocadoes are *amazing* brain foods. Add some blueberries and you've got one incredible brain boosting smoothie. And you can't even taste the avocado!

Yields: 2 Servings

Ingredients:

- ½ avocado, pitted and peeled
- 165g mango
- 4 strawberries
- 75g blueberries
- Ice as needed
- Unsweetened almond milk to max line

Directions:

1. Add the ingredients into the NutriBullet and smash away until smooth.
2. Pour and garnish with a strawberry.
3. Drink and revitalize!

Health Benefits:

- ✓ Very high in vitamins A, B6, C, and E
- ✓ High in dietary fiber
- ✓ Very high in calcium
- ✓ Cholesterol free!

Nutritional values per serving: 215; Total Fat: 12.8g; Cholesterol: 0mg; Sodium: 185mg; Potassium: 625mg; Carbohydrates: 27.4g; Protein: 2.9g

The Great-Goji Smoothie

Goji berries are thought to be the most nutritionally dense food on the planet. Unlike any other plant they contain all the essential amino acids. These amino acids are critical to the production of neurotransmitters which relay messages from our brain to the rest of our body. They are also packed full of vitamins which help keep our brain alert.

Yields: 2 Servings

Ingredients:

- 1-2 handfuls of spinach
- 92g green grapes
- 180g pineapple (fresh or frozen)
- 28g goji berries
- 120ml water
- Ice as needed
- Stevia to taste

Directions:

1. Combine all the ingredients in your NutriBullet and blitz until smooth.
2. Garnish with a wedge of pineapple.
3. Drink and get healthy from all the vitamins!

Health Benefits:

- ✓ Very high in vitamins A and C
- ✓ Very high in manganese
- ✓ Very high in iron
- ✓ High in dietary fiber
- ✓ Low in sodium
- ✓ Very low in saturated fat
- ✓ Cholesterol free!

Nutritional values per serving: Calories: 123; Total Fat: 1.0g; Cholesterol: 0mg; Sodium: 26mg; Potassium: 345mg; Carbohydrates: 29.2g; Protein: 2g

The Kapricot Smoothie

Controlling your blood pressure is vitally important to the prevention of strokes, migraines, and headaches. Apricots are rich in potassium which helps regulate blood pressure and aid in brain development. Kale is also a source of potassium as well as many other beneficial nutrients for healthy brain function.

Yields: 2 Servings

Ingredients:

- 1-2 handfuls of kale
- 3 apricots, pitted
- 1 frozen banana
- 4 strawberries
- water to max line

Directions:

1. Toss all the ingredients into your NutriBullet and power it up for 30 to 60 seconds.
2. Pour and garnish with some fruit.
3. Enjoy!

Health Benefits:

- ✓ Very high in vitamins A, B6 and C
- ✓ High in potassium and manganese
- ✓ High in dietary fiber
- ✓ Low in sodium
- ✓ Very low in saturated fat
- ✓ Cholesterol free!

Nutritional values per serving: Calories: 122; Total Fat: 0.3g; Cholesterol: 0mg; Sodium: 30mg; Potassium: 731mg; Carbohydrates: 29.1g; Protein: 3.6g

Strawberry Banabroc Smoothie

Broccoli is a rich source of antioxidants, vitamins and minerals. Our brains need antioxidants to protect them from free radical damage. They do this by binding themselves to the fee radical on a molecular level. The bananas and the other fruits, especially the strawberries, also provide antioxidants as well as being rich in other brain supporting vitamins and minerals.

Yields: 2 Servings

Ingredients:

- 1 frozen banana
- 50g frozen broccoli
- ½ pear, pitted
- 8 strawberries
- 240ml unsweetened almond milk

Directions:

1. Combine all the ingredients in your NutriBullet and blitz until smooth.
2. Pour and garnish with some fruit and bendy/twisty straws.
3. Drink and get healthy from all the vitamins!

Health Benefits:

- ✓ Very high in vitamins B6, C, and E
- ✓ High in potassium and manganese
- ✓ High in dietary fiber
- ✓ Very low in saturated fat
- ✓ Very high in calcium
- ✓ Cholesterol free!

Nutritional values per serving: Calories: 118; Total Fat: 1.6g; Cholesterol: 0mg; Sodium: 99mg; Potassium: 520mg; Carbohydrates: 26.4g; Protein: 2.3g

Chocolate Cherry Acai Smoothie

Acai berries contain theobromine, a stimulant related to caffeine and when included in your smoothie it will help improve your brain function and concentration. Acai berries are considered a 'super food' for their wide range of vitamins and minerals, and for their concentration of antioxidants and phytochemicals, all of which aid and stimulate our brains.

Yields: 2 Servings

Ingredients:

- 1-2 handfuls of spinach
- 1 frozen banana
- 78g cherries, pits removed
- 1 pouch frozen acai puree
- 1 tablespoon raw cacao powder
- stevia to taste
- 240ml unsweetened almond milk

Directions:

1. Tip all the ingredients into the NutriBullet and fire away until smooth.
2. Guzzle down and grow healthy!

Health Benefits:

- ✓ Very high in vitamins A, C, and E
- ✓ Low in saturated fat
- ✓ High in calcium and manganese
- ✓ Cholesterol free!

Nutritional values per serving: Calories: 153; Total Fat: 2g; Cholesterol: 0mg; Sodium: 141mg; Potassium: 494mg; Carbohydrates: 21.6g; Protein: 11.4g

The All 3 Smoothie

Our brains need sufficient supply of the 3 macronutrients in order to function properly for extended periods. The 3 macronutrients are fats (which help our brains regenerate), protein (which our brains need to produce neurotransmitters), and carbohydrates for energy. Luckily you can find a good amount of all 3 macronutrients in this delicious smoothie. Brain food indeed.

Yields: 2 Servings

Ingredients:

- 1-2 handfuls of kale
- 1 frozen banana
- 360g fresh or frozen pineapple chunks
- 2 tablespoons almond or peanut butter
- unsweetened almond milk or to max line

Directions:

1. Place all the ingredients into the NutriBullet and fire it up until smooth.
2. Sip and grow strong!

Health Benefits:

- ✓ Very high in vitamins A, B6, C, and E
- ✓ Very high in manganese
- ✓ High in calcium
- ✓ Cholesterol free!

Nutritional values per serving: Calories: 292; Total Fat: 10.8g; Cholesterol: 0mg; Sodium: 285mg; Potassium: 994mg; Carbohydrates: 46.2g; Protein: 8.5g

Blue Pomegranate Smoothie

Our brains burn up a lot of energy when we work hard and need to concentrate for long periods. To keep our brains fuelled up and to avoid fatigue we need to take on natural sugars and vitamins as well as taking care to keep hydrated. The blueberries and pomegranate are especially good for your brain, while the watermelon is full of hydrating electrolytes.

Yields: 2 Servings

Ingredients:

- 2 apples, cored
- 152g watermelon
- 240ml pomegranate juice
- 150g blueberries
- Ice as needed

Directions:

1. Place all the ingredients into the NutriBullet and blaze away until smooth.
2. Suck down your delicious smoothie!

Health Benefits:

- ✓ High in vitamins B6 and C
- ✓ High in dietary fiber
- ✓ Very low in sodium
- ✓ Very low in saturated fat
- ✓ Cholesterol free!

Nutritional values per serving: Calories: 234; Total Fat: 0.3g; Cholesterol: 0mg; Sodium: 8mg; Potassium 635mg; Carbohydrates: 59.9g; Protein: 1g

Berry Beet Smoothie

The humble beet is high in fiber, beta carotene, folate, phytonutrients, and natural nitrates that help increase blood flow to the brain. The more blood that enters the brain, the more oxygen there is that gets delivered, which means you can think clearly, concentrate and focus. The coconut oil contributes to this smoothie as a healthy fat which further enhances brain health. But no worries, if you don't have coconut oil you can use a tablespoon of olive oil instead which is also a brain healthy fat (and you won't even taste it).

Yields: 1 Serving

Ingredients:

- 1 medium beet – peeled and chopped
- 75g blueberries
- 8 strawberries
- 1 tablespoon coconut oil
- 1 teaspoon fresh lime juice
- Ice as needed
- 240ml water
- Stevia if desired

Directions:

1. Tip all the ingredients into your blender and blitz them until smooth.
2. Drink and enjoy!

Health benefits:

- ✓ Very high in vitamins B6 and C
- ✓ Very high in manganese
- ✓ Very high in dietary fiber
- ✓ Low in sodium
- ✓ Cholesterol Free!

Nutritional values per serving: Calories: 260; Total Fats: 14.5g; Cholesterol: 0mg; Sodium: 80mg; Potassium: 632mg; Carbohydrates: 35.2g; Protein: 3.4g

Peach Mango Tea Smoothie

Green tea contains caffeine which when used in the right quantities helps stimulate the brain and sharpen our responses to our environment, but without the crash. Exercising or using our brain at its peak performance helps slow the effects of aging. Coconut oil contains all the essential fats that our brain requires in order to regenerate and repair.

Yields: 2 Servings

Ingredients:

- 2 oranges, peeled and quartered
- 165g mango
- ½ peach, pitted
- 2 tsps. coconut oil
- 1 tsp honey
- Ice as needed
- green tea to max line

Directions:

1. Pour steaming hot water into a large glass and add 2 green tea bags. Allow to brew for 3 minutes. Remove tea bags, add honey, and stir. Let the tea cool to room temperature.
2. Combine all the ingredients in your NutriBullet and blitz until smooth.
3. Pour and garnish with a slice of orange.
4. Drink and enjoy!

Health Benefits:

- ✓ Very high in vitamins A and C
- ✓ High in dietary fiber
- ✓ Very low in sodium
- ✓ Cholesterol free!

Nutritional values per serving: Calories: 202; Total Fat: 5g; Cholesterol: 0mg; Sodium: 2mg; Potassium: 506mg; Carbohydrates: 40.4g; Protein: 2.4g

Energy Boosting Smoothies

In today's fast paced, money orientated world we are all a little over extended. Men are working longer hours or moonlighting with second jobs and women are largely back in the work force, juggling a career and kids like a crazy circus act. Corporate pressures often mean that work doesn't end after your 8 hour shift – there are clients to schmooze, events to attend and I'm sure many of us feel like we could happily mainline caffeine to get through it all. What people achieve in one day now probably took a week 50 years ago! If we make it through the day, we get home tired, exhausted and drained and many of us wake up feeling the same way.

Many people are turning to artificial sources for the extra stimulation and energy to deal with our ever overflowing plates. This is naturally not only a dangerous practice but extremely unhealthy and puts untold strain on an already stressed body.

Energy boosting smoothies are the perfect go-to solution. There are a host of ingredients that you can use to jazz up an ordinary smoothie to give you that extra zing to get you through the day and the best part is that they are 100% natural – they are going to nourish you, not drain you further. One of the dangers of artificial stimulants is that they work well to perk you up, but when the "high" wears off, you are left feeling even more drained, forcing you to take more to combat the cyclical fatigue that threatens to push you over the edge. These smoothies are also a great option for a pre-workout energy boost as they give you enough vooma to really get the most out of your workout.

So if you are feeling tired and sluggish, try some of these energy boosting ingredients to put the spring back in your step and keep it there. Maca powder comes from the maca root and is high in carbohydrates and glucose which will keep your engine running from morning until night. Chia seeds were used by the South American warriors to give them the stamina and energy to run for days with just a handful of these magical seeds to keep them going. Goji berries are a low GI option to energize you as they are ranked 29/100 on the glycemic index but contain a host of energizing nutrients. Green tea contains caffeine in the perfect ratio to boost your energy without the tell-tale jitters of coffee. Spirulina is very high in protein and thus is a sustained source of natural energy. In addition, it is very high in the B vitamins which help activate the body to burn its fat stores for energy.

Go forth and revitalize your body, mind and soul!

Magic Maca Smoothie

The maca root is native to the high Andes in Peru, particularly the lake Junin area. It is best in powder form and provides a powerful boost of energy when you include it in your smoothies, without crashing later or any negative side effects. It even improves memory, migraines, and sex drive! Plus the cacao is an energy booster as well. Drink this smoothie in the morning and go forth to conquer your day.

Yields: 1 Serving

Ingredients:

- 123g raspberries
- 1 frozen banana
- 1 tablespoon raw cacao powder
- 1 tablespoon raw maca powder
- ½ tsp vanilla extract
- Stevia to taste
- 240ml unsweetened almond milk

Directions:

1. Place all the ingredients in your NutriBullet and fire it up until smooth.
2. Sip this yummy smoothie and blast off to the horizon!

Health Benefits:

- ✓ Very high in vitamins B6, C, and E
- ✓ High in manganese
- ✓ High in dietary fiber
- ✓ Very high in calcium
- ✓ Low in saturated fat
- ✓ Cholesterol free!

Nutritional values per serving: Calories: 229; Total Fat: 3.4g; Cholesterol: 0mg; Sodium: 187mg; Potassium: 816mg; Carbohydrates: 45.3g; Protein: 5g

Apple Green Tea Smoothie

Green tea has caffeine in it which helps stimulate our body. When you combine it with the carbohydrates and vitamins from the other ingredients you get a smoothie which will boost your immediate energy levels, while still having enough energy reserves to fuel you until your next meal.

Yields: 2 Servings

Ingredients:

- 1-2 handfuls of spinach
- 1 apple, cored
- 240ml green tea
- ½ avocado, pitted and peeled
- 123g raspberries (or any berry)
- few mint leaves
- stevia to taste
- ice as needed
- unsweetened almond milk to max line

Directions:

1. Pour steaming hot water into a glass and add 2 green tea bags. Allow to brew for 3 minutes. Remove tea bags, add honey, and stir. Let tea cool to room temperature.
2. Place all the ingredients into the NutriBullet and fire it up until smooth.
3. Slurp down this delicious healthy smoothie.

Health Benefits:

- ✓ Very high in vitamins A, B6, C, and E
- ✓ High in manganese
- ✓ High in potassium
- ✓ High in dietary fiber
- ✓ Very high in calcium
- ✓ Cholesterol free!

Nutritional values per serving: Calories: 189; Total Fat: 12.4g; Cholesterol: 0mg; Sodium: 208mg; Potassium: 686mg; Carbohydrates: 19.6g; Protein: 2.9g

The Chiavacado Smoothie

Chia seeds are a rich source of complex carbohydrates, and provide a major energy boost. Even better, they don't give a huge insulin spike which avoids the crash and burn. The avocado in this smoothie is also important as the fats are a great source of energy for our muscles and brains. Add some pomegranate juice and you have a yummy energizer.

Yields: 2 Servings

Ingredients:

- ½ avocado, pitted and peeled
- 2 apricots
- 150g mixed berries
- 2 tablespoons chia seeds
- Ice as needed
- 240ml pomegranate juice
- Water to max line

Directions:

1. Add the ingredients into the NutriBullet and smash away until smooth.
2. Pour and garnish with a twisty/bendy straw and a slice of apricot.
3. Drink and revitalize your body!

Health Benefits:

- ✓ Very high in vitamins B6 and C
- ✓ High in manganese
- ✓ High in dietary fiber
- ✓ Very low in sodium
- ✓ Cholesterol free!

Nutritional values per serving: Calories: 265; Total Fat: 12.7g; Cholesterol: 0mg; Sodium: 9mg; Potassium: 740mg; Carbohydrates: 40.2g; Protein: 3.5g

Coconut Goji Smoothie

Goji berries are an excellent source of energy. They have a low glycemic index value and yet still restore strength and energize. The cacao powder contains the right amount of good fats and protein needed for a sustained energy release, while the coconut milk provides energy for an immediate boost.

Yields: 2 Servings

Ingredients:

- 1 -2 handfuls of kale
- 1 frozen banana
- 28g goji berries
- 2 tablespoons raw cacao powder
- 240ml coconut milk
- Stevia to taste
- 60ml water if needed

Directions:

1. Pour all the ingredients into your NutriBullet and blast them until smooth.
2. Decant the smoothie into two suitable cups and garnish with twisty/ bendy straws and a cocktail umbrella.
3. Drink up and get healthy and alert!

Health Benefits:

- ✓ Very high in vitamins A and C
- ✓ High in iron
- ✓ High in manganese
- ✓ Very low in sodium
- ✓ Cholesterol free!

Nutritional values per serving: Calories: 436; Total Fat: 30.4g; Cholesterol: 0mg; Sodium: 50mg; Potassium: 856mg; Carbohydrates: 39g; Protein: 5.7g

Papaya Lime Smoothie

Spirulina is nature's version of an energy drink. Its natural nitric oxide provides immediate and enduring physical and mental energy. A cup of papaya not only gives you an energy boost, but also helps protect against the potential damages of secondhand smoke, rheumatoid arthritis and common cold. When combined with the yoghurt in the smoothie, it will provide a long healthy boost of energy for your brain and muscles.

Yields: 2 Servings

Ingredients:

- 300g papaya/pawpaw, pitted
- 1 apricot (or ½ peach)
- Juice of 1 lime
- 68g fat free Greek yoghurt
- 1 teaspoon Spirulina
- Ice as needed
- unsweetened almond milk to max line

Directions:

1. Tip all the ingredients into the NutriBullet and fire away until smooth.
2. Guzzle down and feel rejuvenated!

Health Benefits:

- ✓ Very high in vitamins A, C, and E
- ✓ High in thiamin and riboflavin
- ✓ High in potassium and iron
- ✓ High in dietary fiber
- ✓ Very high in calcium
- ✓ Very low in saturated fat
- ✓ Cholesterol free!

Nutritional values per serving: Calories: 132; Total Fat: 3g; Cholesterol: 0mg; Sodium: 216mg; Potassium: 517mg; Carbohydrates: 20.5g; Protein: 7g

Kalefornia Dreaming Smoothie

Kale is the most well-known cruciferous or leafy green vegetable 'super food' and for good reason! It has a high vitamin content as well as containing most of the essential minerals we need. But it also a great energy booster and form of calcium. The coconut has the good fats we need for energy and the orange and lemon add a nice zing.

Yields: 2 Servings

Ingredients:

- 1-2 handfuls of kale
- 1 frozen banana
- 2 oranges, peeled
- Juice of 1 lemon
- Ice as needed
- Stevia to taste
- 240ml coconut milk (or coconut water)

Directions:

1. Place all the ingredients into the NutriBullet and blaze away until smooth.
2. Suck down your energy boosting smoothie!

Health Benefits:

- ✓ Very high in vitamins A and C
- ✓ High in manganese
- ✓ Very low in sodium
- ✓ Cholesterol free!

Nutritional values per serving; Calories: 448; Total Fat: 28.8g; Cholesterol: 0mg; Sodium: 48mg; Potassium: 1189mg; Carbohydrates: 48.7g; Protein: 7.1g

The Not-a-Nut Smoothie

Contrary to popular belief the almond is not a nut but is actually classified as a seed. None-the-less it is, like nuts, a very good source of protein and good fats and iron which is essential to maintaining energy levels. Broccoli is loaded with vitamin B which helps the body release stored fats for energy. The apple and banana are excellent sources of ready to burn carbohydrates. All at only 148 calories per serving!

Yields: 2 Servings

Ingredients:

- 1 peach, pitted
- 1 frozen banana
- 50g frozen broccoli
- 27g slivered raw almonds
- water to max line

Directions:

1. Combine all the ingredients in your NutriBullet and blitz until smooth.
2. Drink and get busy from all the vitamins!

Health Benefits:

- ✓ Very high in vitamin C
- ✓ High in manganese
- ✓ High in dietary fiber
- ✓ Low in saturated fat
- ✓ Very low in sodium
- ✓ Cholesterol free!

Nutritional values per serving: Calories: 148; Total Fat: 6.1g; Cholesterol: 0mg; Sodium: 8mg; Potassium: 463mg; Carbohydrates: 22.2g; Protein: 4.2g

Peach Walnut Smoothie

Walnuts are a great tasting addition to any smoothie and they are high in protein which keeps you going for the long haul. The oats provide a slow release of energy over the morning, while the peaches help provide carbohydrates to fuel you through the day.

Yields: 2 Servings

Ingredients:

- 2 tablespoons dry oats
- 1 large peach, pitted
- 30g walnuts
- ½ teaspoon vanilla extract
- 1 tablespoon honey
- Ice as needed
- 360ml unsweetened almond milk

Directions:

1. Toss all the ingredients into your NutriBullet and power it up until smooth.
2. Pour and garnish with a twisty/bendy straw and some fruit.
3. Enjoy!

Health Benefits:

- ✓ High in vitamin E
- ✓ High in manganese
- ✓ High in calcium
- ✓ Low in saturated fat
- ✓ Cholesterol free!

Nutritional values per serving: Calories: 204; Total Fat: 11.6g; Cholesterol: 0mg; Sodium: 136mg; Potassium: 384mg; Carbohydrates: 22g; Protein: 5.9g

Coconut-Lime Smoothie

Coconuts and coconut oil contain MCT's (medium-chain triglycerides) which provide a natural energy source to the body. Flax meal (or ground flax seeds) are rich in oil which is a high energy nutrient. Combine the two with the wonderful flavor of honeydew melon and lime, and you've got something pretty amazing... and energizing!

Yields: 2 Servings

Ingredients:

- 1-2 handfuls of spinach
- 1 frozen banana
- 315g honeydew melon
- Few slices cucumber
- Juice of ½ lime
- Few mint leaves
- 1 tablespoon flax meal
- 120ml coconut milk
- 1 tablespoon coconut oil

Directions:

1. Throw all the ingredients into your NutriBullet and blitz until smooth.
2. Consume and power your engine for longer!

Health Benefits:

- ✓ Very high in vitamins A and C
- ✓ High in manganese
- ✓ Low in sodium
- ✓ Cholesterol free!

Nutritional values per serving: Calories: 339 Total Fat: 22.8g; Cholesterol: 0mg; Sodium: 65mg; Potassium: 1021mg; Carbohydrates: 35.9g; Protein: 4.8g

Apricot Watermelon Smoothie

They don't sell apricot energy bars for nothing. Apricots are not only delicious, but provide a great source of energy. Hemp seeds also help to build your energy levels while the watermelon and orange hydrate and create a unique tasty flavor. Drink up and be energized! (If you don't have apricots, use pears instead. They work well in this smoothie and pear juice also provides a quick and natural source of energy.)

Yields: 2 Servings

Ingredients:

- 2-4 handfuls chopped Romaine lettuce
- 2 apricots, pitted (or 2 pears)
- 305g watermelon
- 1 orange, peeled
- 1 tablespoon hemp seeds

Directions:

1. Combine all the ingredients in your NutriBullet and blitz until smooth.
2. Drink and enjoy!

Health Benefits:

- ✓ Very high in vitamins A, B6, and C
- ✓ High in potassium and iron
- ✓ High in dietary fiber
- ✓ High in dietary fiber
- ✓ Low in saturated fat
- ✓ Cholesterol free!

Nutritional values per serving: Calories: 140; Total Fat: 2.9g; Cholesterol: 0mg; Sodium: 5mg; Potassium: 564mg; Carbohydrates: 28.8g; Protein: 4.2g

Conclusion

And that's a wrap everyone. This book should meet all your smoothie needs, green and non-green alike, but it is by no means exhaustive. The beauty of smoothies is their versatility. Swop out what you don't like (or what you don't have) and replace it with what you do. Make it fun and enjoy yourself experimenting with different combinations of ingredients. Get the kids involved and make smoothies a family affair to be enjoyed by young and old.

With the NutriBullet in your smoothie arsenal, you cannot go wrong and are guaranteed a rewarding experience. It makes the whole process so easy, you will wonder why you didn't get one years ago!

And most importantly when you drink them, clink your glasses and salute to your good health – it is only going to get better, I promise!

Until next time – ciao!

Diana Clayton

Recommendations

... More Low Calorie Goodness!

Hungry for more? Pick up the latest editions of low calorie books from Diana. Just search Amazon for "Diana Clayton" and discover even *more* incredible recipes, all while shedding some pounds. Diana's low calorie cookbook collection includes ....

Amazon Bestseller!

Slow Cooker Recipe Book: *Dieter's Paradise*:

Heavenly Slow Cooker Recipes
from All Around the World,
All Under 500 Calories!

Amazon Feature!

5:2 Diet Recipe Book,
All Under 300 Calories

Healthy & Filling 5:2 Fast Diet Recipes to Lose Weight and Enhance your Health

Fan Favorite!

5:2 Fast Diet Recipe Book:
Meals for One!

Amazing Single Serving 5:2 Fast Diet Recipes to Lose More Weight with Intermittent Fasting

Must Have!

Slim Smoothies

Healthy & Nutritious Smoothie Recipes for Weight Loss, Improved Health, and Happiness

NutriBullet Series!

Savoury Soups

Healthy & Nutritious NutriBullet Soup Recipes for Weight Loss, Improved Health, and Happiness

And much more to come . . .

Enjoy!

Index

References are to page numbers.

Printed in Great Britain
by Amazon.co.uk, Ltd.,
Marston Gate.